THE GREEN AND RED PLANET

HUBERTUS
STRUGHOLD
Professor of Aviation Medicine
Head of Department of Space Medicine
U. S. Air Force School of Aviation Medicine

With Editorial Assistance
And a Foreword by

GREEN
PEYTON

THE UNIVERSITY O

A

Physiological

Study of the

Possibility

of Life on

MARS

THE GREEN AND RED PLANET

NEW MEXICO PRESS

Library of Congress
Catalog Card Number:
53-8894

To MAJOR GENERAL
HARRY G. ARMSTRONG, USAF (MC)

whose pioneer experiments
in high-altitude physiology
have done so much to make
this study possible

FOREWORD

Ever since 1609, when Galileo Galilei built the first astronomical telescope and confirmed the belief of Copernicus that the sun is the center of our universe, scholars and artists have speculated on the delightful possibility that there might be living creatures similar to ourselves on the other planets of our solar system. Long before, the moon had been a favorite subject for imaginary voyages such as that of Lucian of Samos in his *True History,* published in the second century after Christ. But it was Galileo's substantiation of the number and variety of other worlds that roused the curiosity of men who long to roam beyond this troubled planet.

Within a few years after Galileo's announcement, the Dutch physicist Christian Huygens—who shared with him the discovery of the rings of Saturn—declared his belief that the other planets are populated by beings whose chemical constituents are different from ours. In 1686, the French writer Bernard de Fontenelle, in his *Treatise on the Multiplicity of Worlds,* described their inhabitants in exhaustive detail, following the theories of Huygens.

The great Voltaire, in 1752, wrote a satire called *Micromégas,* in which a gigantic traveler from a planet of the star Sirius visited the earth in company with a friend from Saturn, and made sardonic comments on our customs and behavior. Even Immanuel Kant, the father of modern philosophy, took for granted in his *Natural History of the Heavens* that the other planets are the home of people reasonably like ourselves.

In our own time, H. G. Wells started a craze for speculative romances with *The War of the Worlds,* in which a race of monstrous creatures from Mars invades the earth and eventually is destroyed by microbes which did not exist on their planet. And, of course, side by side with these fantastic writings, are those of scientists such as the American astronomer Percival Lowell, who devoted his life to the attempt to prove that intelligent beings must exist on Mars.

In all the literature about the possibility of life on other planets, a striking fact emerges. These passionate arguments and rapturous romances invariably have been written by astronomers or story tellers—never by an authority on the conditions that make life possible and the ways in which it might adapt itself to the peculiar circumstances found on the other planets of our solar universe.

If we wish to inquire about life, it is only sensible that we should go to a biologist, whose specialty is the study of living matter. If we wish to examine its behavior in a strange environment, we should consult a physiologist, whose preoccupation is the function of living things in the various unlikely milieux where they may be found.

It would be impossible to find a person more eminently suited for the study which is the subject of this book than the scholar who has written it. Dr. Hubertus Strughold for the past twenty-five years has been examining life in the most complicated surroundings that support it on earth: in the high reaches of the atmosphere which have been made accessible to man only since the development of flight, less than a half-century ago.

Dr. Strughold is a pioneer in one of the newest sciences, opened up by the Wright Brothers' achievement: the field of aviation medicine. Born in Westphalia, Germany, he studied medicine and natural sciences at the universities of Muenster, Goettingen, Munich, and Wuerzburg. He He took his Ph.D. from Muenster in 1922, his M.D. from Wuerzburg in 1923. From the start he specialized in the medicine of flight, at a time when only a few physiologists in this country and abroad were concerned about the remarkable effects on human tissue brought about by ascending a few thousand feet into the sky.

In 1928-29, Dr. Strughold was a fellow of the Rockefeller Foundation, pursuing his researches at Western Reserve University in Cleveland and at the University of Chicago. He returned to Germany to teach at Wuerzburg until, in 1935, he became director of the Aeromedical

Research Institute in Berlin. Four years later he joined an associate in bringing out the authoritative German textbook, *Basic Principles of Aviation Medicine.*

At the end of the War, the study of aviation medicine seemed to be a dead issue in Germany. Dr. Strughold accepted a post as professor of physiology at the University of Heidelberg. He was there when, in 1947, a representative of the United States Air Force School of Aviation Medicine discovered him and invited him to join the staff of that still-thriving aeromedical institution. Dr. Strughold has been at Randolph Field, Texas, ever since.

In 1949, when Major General Harry G. Armstrong, now Surgeon General of the Air Force but then commandant of the School, created the department of Space Medicine, Dr. Strughold was placed in charge of it. The department was the result of General Armstrong's realization that jet and rocket aircraft were taking men into a region so far above the ground that it was physiologically indistinguishable from space. Soon afterward, the Air University—which includes under its command all the educational functions of the Air Force—conferred on Dr. Strughold the academic title, Professor of Aviation Medicine. He is the only person who has been so honored.

Dr. Strughold himself makes it clear in this book that the study of aviation medicine—especially under the high-altitude conditions of modern flight—has cast a peculiar illumination on the problems of life in space and on the other planets which are our neighbors in the cosmos. As the reader will discover, the conditions under which life would have to exist on Venus or Mars—and particularly on Mars—are remarkably like the circumstances confronting a flyer in the remote upper air above the earth.

The parallel has led Dr. Strughold to ask himself: "What are the possibilities for life on other planets?"

From his inquiry has issued the book which you now hold in your hand. Starting with the physical data compiled by two generations of astronomers and physicists, Dr. Strughold has subjected the question to the sharp scrutiny of a brilliant physiological mind and has arrived at the most complete, the most exact definition of the biological possibilities of other planets that is conceivable until such time as we can visit them.

One intriguing byway of this question Dr. Strughold deliberately avoids. It is the very one that Huygens raised in the seventeenth century, and Fontenelle shortly afterward: the possibility that life based on a totally different chemical process might be found on Mars or another planet. But this sort of speculation is not in Dr. Strughold's province. Fascinating though it is, he eschews it because his duty as a physiologist is to examine the processes of life as he knows them.

Exploration in the universe might someday prove that Dr. Strughold is quite wrong in his conclusions, as he well knows. But until the irrefutable evidence of experience shows him to be wrong, his conclusions cannot well be questioned. They are based on all the knowledge of life available to us at this time on this planet, and we are not likely to find much more until we travel far outside the confines of our own atmosphere—that sea of air from which, as Dr. Strughold has elsewhere said, our emergence is comparable to the first migration of living creatures onto dry land from the boundless ocean.

GREEN PEYTON

San Antonio, Texas
1 June 1953

PREFACE

The planet Mars, to the naked eye, appears in the starry night sky as a spot of pale red color, conspicuous among the yellow spangles around it. Because of this it often is called "the Red Planet."

In the telescope, too, it is seen ordinarily as a little reddish disc. But at a certain season of the Martian year, green or blue-green areas appear. After several months they change into yellow, and finally into chocolate brown, still noticeable against the generally ruddy hue of the planet's surface as a whole.

These areas were observed by the astronomer Percival Lowell early in this century, and since then they have been described often in astronomical literature. Because they remind us very much of the seasonal discolorations caused by the growth of plant life on our own planet, they have been interpreted as a sign of vegetation on Mars.

Indeed, the green component in the telescopic picture of Mars has made that planet an object of serious biological discussion by writers on astronomy. It is this green component which has impelled me, as a biologist, to consider the possibility of life on Mars. This book is in its essence, then, a biological study. To make this fact plain, I have added the "green" to the usual "red" in the title. The green that might be vegetation is what primarily concerns me here, not the red which is the most obvious aspect of the planet to an observer.

Because of its predominantly biological character, this book may serve as an addition to those which have already been written about Mars by astronomers. In discussing the significance of the green areas, these authors have dealt with the subject mainly from the point of view of the physicist. This is, I believe, the first study of Mars made by a physiologist; and in writing it I am most fortunate to be able to draw on the wealth of astronomical knowledge which their writings provide.

To keep the discussion as simple as possible—and also to avoid needless repetition—I have touched only briefly in the development of this subject on details which have been studied exhaustively by others. For example, Harold Spencer Jones in his book, *Life on Other Worlds,* published in 1940, devotes a full chapter to the structure of the carbon atom and its versatile function in the processes of life. The importance of the carbon atom is mentioned here, but it has not seemed to me necessary to retrace the ground which Spencer Jones has covered so thoroughly. For those readers who may wish to probe deeper into this and other absorbing questions of biology and physics, a bibliography of the main sources I have used is given at the end of the book.

This treatise is by no means confined to a discussion of the green component—that is to say, the question of vegetation on Mars. Rather, it examines generally the possibility that living matter, as we know it, might exist on that planet. For comparative reasons, such an examination must extend also in some degree to the other planets, and especially to the earth. Thus it goes into a new and unexplored field of biology, which may be termed general planetary ecology—the science of planets as an environment for life.

From its biological nature, other implications of the book may become evident. They include a better understanding of the peculiar position of our own favored planet as the apparent biocenter of the solar system, and a firmer realization of the physical limitations of life on earth, both horizontally—according to its geographic and climatic distribution—and vertically, in its distribution downward into the sea and upward into the reaches of our atmosphere. These are problems which are of the greatest interest to the ecological geographer and to the specialist in aviation medicine. Both of these fields—especially aviation medicine with its new branch, space medicine—have contributed a rich store of information which is pertinent to the study of Mars.

Acknowledgments

First I must express my appreciation to the people of the United States for their hospitality in welcoming me to this country and in making it possible for me to continue my research. The courtesies extended to me by my neighbors, my associates, and indeed by utter strangers have given me the confidence to carry on with studies such as this.

In particular I wish to thank the Surgeon General of the Air Force, Major General Harry G. Armstrong, to whom this book is dedicated, and his successor as Commandant of the School of Aviation Medicine, Brigadier General Otis O. Benson, Jr. Under their far-seeing and beneficent administration I have been granted the widest freedom in my work. Their encouragement of pure science has produced at Randolph Field a climate in which I could pursue investigations of this kind, even though they are not immediately connected with any military project.

For much lucid and enlightening information I am grateful to my colleagues, Dr. Heinz Haber, who is now associated with the University of California at Los Angeles, Dr. Fritz Haber, Dr. Hans G. Clamann, and Dr. Ulrich Cameron Luft. In many provocative discussions they have made suggestions of the utmost value in the task of reconciling astrophysical and physiological data.

To Dr. E. C. Slipher and Dr. V. M. Slipher of the Lowell Observatory in Flagstaff, Arizona, I am doubly indebted—first for the knowledge of Mars which they have accumulated and made available to students like myself, and again for their hospitality on the occasion of several visits to Mars Hill. By continuing the observations of Percival Lowell after his death in 1916, these two distinguished astronomers have immeasurably advanced our understanding of the green and red planet.

They kindly arranged for me an examination of Mars through the 42-inch telescope at Flagstaff. Without this personal view of the areas discussed here, I could not have considered my work complete. Also they have been gracious enough to let me use photographs showing the progress of the seasons on that planet, reproduced as the series in Plate I.

My thanks are extended to Dr. Lincoln LaPaz of the Institute of Meteoritics of the University of New Mexico and to Dr. Clayton S. White of the Lovelace Foundation, for reviewing the manuscript. Their opinions, and those of other scientists who have read various passages of it, are much appreciated.

Finally, I wish to thank Mr. Merrill D. Doyle, scientific illustrator at the School of Aviation Medicine, for the charts and drawings which he has prepared for the book.

HUBERTUS STRUGHOLD

Randolph Field, Texas
1 June 1953

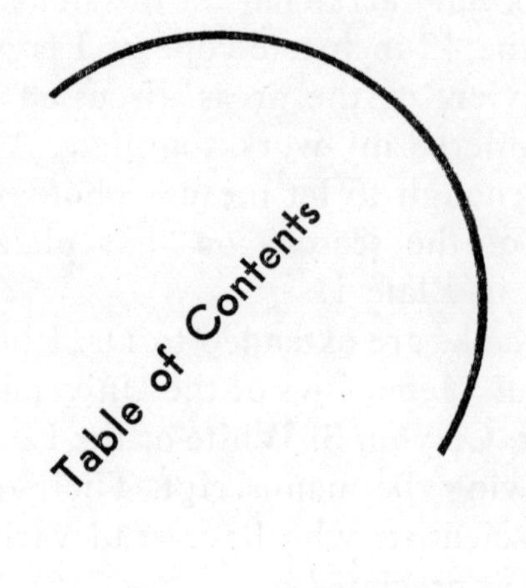
Table of Contents

Illustrations

FIGURES

PLATES

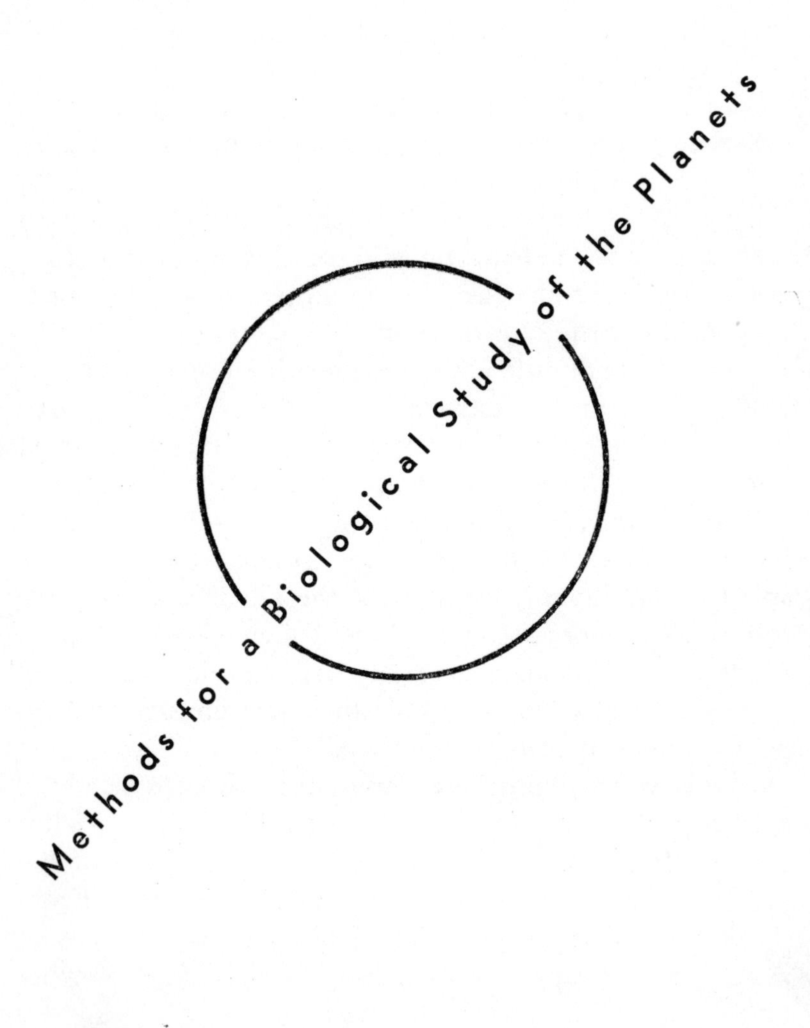

1

"It is necessary," said Aristotle, "that we study the stars." From our study of them arose the most ancient of all our sciences, astronomy. It is indeed necessary that astronomers give us our basic knowledge of the stars. But today the words of the Greek philosopher present a challenge also to the more recent science of biology.

Early man studied the heavens first for guidance in computing the seasons as an aid to agriculture, and later for assistance in navigation, and still later to enlarge his knowledge of the cosmos. Now, as the time approaches when we may be able to travel to some of our neighbors in space, we search the stars for an answer to another question: Is there life elsewhere in the universe?

"Up to the middle of the nineteenth century," Percival Lowell once wrote, "astronomy was busied with motions. The wanderings of the planets in their courses attracted attention . . . to the practical exclusion of all else concerning them. . . . But when the century that has gone was halfway through its course, a change came over the spirit of the investigation; with the advance in physics, celestial searchers began to concern themselves with matter, too. Gravitational astronomy had regarded the planets from the point of view of how they act; physical astronomy is intent upon what they are."

To Lowell's definitions there should perhaps be added a third, which might be called astrobiology, as distinguished from astrophysics. It is the investigation of the planets with regard to their habitability for life. From the known facts of what the planets are, it proceeds to ask: Can they support living beings—and, if so, of what kind?

Until lately, such questions had of necessity to be left in the vague realm of speculation. But with the fresh information on life in unfamiliar environments turned up in the last few years by aviation medicine, it becomes possible at last to suggest some answers. They must, as a matter of course, be given by the biologist, using the physical data compiled by astronomers and physicists. And the most adequate tools for such an inquiry are to be found in the study of ecology, a modern branch of biology.

Ecology is that science which treats of the physical environment of a place or region, with regard to its fitness as a site for the existence and development of living things. This field is known as physical ecology. The science deals also with the adaptive reactions or responses of living things to their environment, in order to make their existence easier wherever they may be; and this is known as physiological ecology.

As a branch of biology, ecology embraces both the biological kingdoms: animals and plants, in the form of human ecology, animal ecology, and plant ecology. Until now, ecology has been applied only to the earth as an environment, often under the name, ecological geography. Extending it to other planets, we enter a new field which may be called planetary ecology.

This science studies all the planets, including the earth, with regard to their comparative fitness as a biological environment. It is well within the legitimate bounds of natural science to examine the ecology of other planets, especially in the area of physical ecology. The aim of all science is to extend our knowledge of life, with the ultimate object of discovering its purpose and the place we occupy in the universe as a whole.

The question of life on other planets is already an old subject of discussion. In modern times it was raised in 1877 with the publication by the Milanese astronomer, Giovanni V. Schiaparelli, of a report on the so-called canals of Mars. The discussion reached its climax in the books of Percival Lowell in 1907 and 1909. Lowell concentrated on the planet Mars, and for this purpose erected a special observatory in Flagstaff, Arizona. His main work is titled, *Mars as the Abode of Life*.

Treatises on the same theme have come from the writings of Camille Flammarion, Svante Arrhenius, E. M. Antoniadi, William H. Pickering, E. C. Slipher, E. W. Maunder, Gerard P. Kuiper, Harold Spencer Jones, and Gérard de Vaucouleurs among others. It is interesting to note that the study of this subject heretofore has been confined almost exclusively to astronomers.

In recent years, several astronomical books and papers have appeared, surveying the latest research on planetary atmospheres. The newer discoveries in this field offer the ecologist and the physiologist a great deal of valuable information which was not available twenty—or even ten—years ago. These advances on the frontiers of astronomy are bound to stimulate the biologist to enter the discussion.

It seems to me all the more necessary to raise the question of life on other planets to the biological plane, where it belongs, when we consider the progress made of late by physiologists in this field. Sparked by aviation medicine and its pioneer offshoot, space medicine, physiological research in the last two or three decades has uncovered some remarkable data on the limitations and behavior of life under various environmental conditions. On the basis of this biological information, we now are able to exclude some manifestations of life on other planets with reasonable certainty, and to consider some others as possible.

This undertaking presupposes the assumption that the laws of biological processes are the same throughout the universe; and this in turn assumes that the structure of all living matter is based on the carbon atom and its unique chemical properties. It is not beyond the range of imagination to conceive that some other base—such as the silicon atom—might be the foundation for a kind of life. But to do so here would be to reach beyond the known facts on which scientific inquiry has to build, and thus would do violence to the object of this book. Therefore we must take the structure of life as we know it for the starting point of our study.

In this work, then, we confine ourselves to known manifestations of life as we find them on this planet. They are sufficiently various and elastic to provide us with a wide enough area for discussion. To the physical environments on other planets we apply the standards of ecology and physiology, insofar as they are valid on earth. In so doing, we can estimate the extent to which life of our kind is possible on other planets.

Life of an utterly different kind would scarcely be life at all, in the sense that we instinctively wish to find beings like ourselves, in a habitat similar to our own, in other regions of the universe. It is, in a manner of speaking, our own species that we are studying in every scientific inquiry we undertake. By examining the possibilities for life on other planets, we acquire at the same time a better knowledge of the limitations and abundance of life on our own singularly blessed earth.

Not only are these matters of general scientific interest and of human significance. Also they are pertinent to another problem of special interest at this time. We live today in an age of highly advanced development in transportation. Already military aircraft are operating in the Arctic regions, in the stratosphere, and even on the borders of space. Within a few more years, jet-powered and rocket-powered commercial craft will follow them into those lofty and remote areas.

This means that men of our era even now are easily carried into the most extreme environments of weather and climatic surroundings here on—and above—the earth, and tomorrow such travel will become general. Aviation medicine (again with its offspring, space medicine) is deeply interested in the physiological effects of those extremes, and in finding protective measures and equipment for those who encounter them. Ecological study of environmental circumstances on other planets can contribute to the picture of conditions on our own, even though at present the study must be theoretical.

No planet offers a better subject for such ecological study than does the planet Mars. An airplane in our atmosphere flying at an altitude of about ten miles (55,000 feet) is already in a terrestrial environment which is closely similar in many respects to that on the surface of Mars. An inquiry into atmospheric conditions on Mars, then, can also help us in meeting the problems of high-altitude flight.

As I have already emphasized in the Preface, this is a biological treatise that differs from other books on biology in one important respect. Here the principles that govern life on earth are extrapolated—as we say in scientific terminology—to the environments found on other planets in our solar system. The astronomical data on which this extrapolation is based is not set down in a separate chapter, but is noted in the text wherever it pertains to the biological discussion. For detailed analyses of the astronomical facts cited, the various publications of the authors mentioned above may be consulted. There, too, the opinions given in astronomical literature about the possibility of life on other planets can be found.

The most impressive, most original, and—so to speak—classical work on the subject is that of Percival Lowell. The opinions of the different writers vary between an enthusiastic affirmation and a flat denial that such life exists. In this book I have tried to treat the question dispassionately from the point of view of a biologist. And, for reasons which will become apparent, I have concentrated primarily on Mars, "the green and red planet." Much information has been collected on the other planets. But Mars is the one that we know best, and the one which has attracted the greatest interest for that reason.

As we shall see, it is also the planet which offers the most inviting prospect of an environment not too unlike our own.

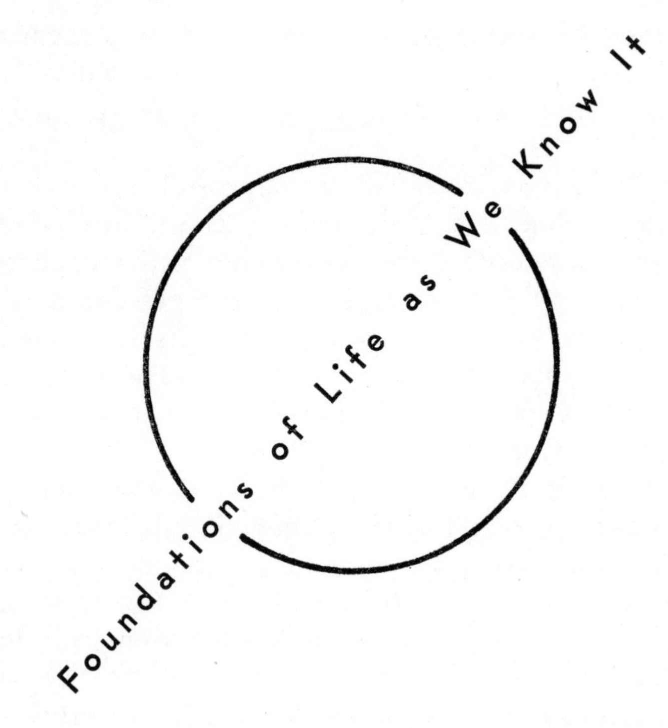

2

To explain all the laws and principles that govern the development of life in its great profusion on our planet is far beyond the scope of this book. On the other hand, if we are to understand the rules that apply in any scientific discussion of the possibility of living organisms on other planets, a brief survey of the physiological foundations of life as we find it on earth is in order. The subject is a vastly complicated one, and many new avenues of approach have been opened lately by chemical and physical research. Here we can only touch with a light hand on the aspects of it that apply to this particular study.

They fall into four convenient categories: 1) the chemical composition of organic matter; 2) the methods by which it is produced; 3) the sources from which its energy is derived; and 4) the ways in which gas (or air) is exchanged between the organism and its surrounding medium—normally the water of seas and lakes and rivers or the earth's enveloping atmosphere. Let us take these four categories in order.

1. All matter is composed of the same basic elements in various degrees and combinations. But all matter is of course not alive. We wish to find those chemical elements which, in proper proportions and under favorable circumstances, provide the unique composition of living matter.

Biochemistry has shown us that the living substance of plants and animals consists of the relatively light elements. They all belong to the lower half of the periodic table of elements by atomic weights, where such materials as helium, nitrogen, and silicon are found, as opposed to the upper half which contains heavy chemicals like tungsten, lead, or uranium.

Thus living matter is a substance of very light-weight construction. This in itself is an intriguing fact, with several fascinating implications. It suggests, for instance, the possibility that life may require for its existence a planet whose gravitation more or less approximates that of the earth. But these are questions which need not concern us here.

One group of the bioelements is found only in small amounts. They include sodium (atomic weight 22.997), magnesium (24.32), silicon (28.06), chlorine (35.457), potassium (39.096), calcium (40.08), iron (55.85), and iodine (126.92), of which the one comparatively heavy chemical is the last. They occur in the form of acids and salts.

Two elements of special interest in this group are magnesium and iron. They are the central atoms in two vital biological pigments. Iron is the basic chemical of hemoglobin, in the red blood corpuscles of animals. Magnesium occurs in chlorophyl, the green coloring matter of plants. Hemoglobin is essential to the process of respiration, by which oxygen is absorbed into the cells, while chlorophyl is required for photosynthesis, by which inorganic materials are converted into food.

The main elements in protoplasm are among the very lightest. They are hydrogen (atomic weight 1.008), carbon (12.01), nitrogen (14.008), and oxygen (16). With them, in certain cases, are associated phosphorus (30.98) and sulphur (32.066). They are found in the form of proteins, fats, and carbohydrates.

In all these living substances carbon invariably is present. Indeed, it is their essential base atom. This unique position of the carbon atom as the basis of life is due mainly to its peculiar atomic structure. It is known as a quadrivalent atom, which means that it has a power of four in forming combinations of atoms, as compared with others that have more or less. Without trying to explain this peculiar virtue, we may simply note that it gives the carbon atom a tremendous potential ability to create more complex structures such as living cells.

Carbon atoms combine with each other up to three valences; or they can unite with other atoms like hydrogen, nitrogen, and oxygen, or with whole groups of atoms.

In this way a great variety of chain and ring compounds can be built up—the total number of them reaches into the millions. It is this tremendous versatility of the carbon atom that makes possible the extreme diversity of life, and its ability to adapt itself to the most improbable conditions.

Another notable characteristic of these carbon compounds is that their reactions proceed slowly under the mysterious influence of the enzymes, giving a certain continuity to living processes. Otherwise—since life is a form of combustion—they would be consumed too rapidly for the organism to translate them into vital activity. Also, the carbon compounds are fairly stable in the range of temperatures which they encounter on earth. And there are other absorbing properties of the carbon atom, which can be studied in detail in Spencer Jones' book, *Life on Other Worlds.*

Of special significance also in the processes of life is water, a compound of hydrogen and oxygen (H_2O). It has many valuable biological properties. Water is the solvent of the various protoplasmic constituents, the agency which permits them to be transferred (as in the blood) from cell to cell, and then inside the cells of the organism. Water plays a vital role in the regulation of body temperature, maintaining it at a point which is favorable to physiological functions. Water is also one of the raw materials for the development of carbohydrates in plants by photosynthesis.

The importance of water as a prerequisite for active life cannot be emphasized too much in planetary ecology, for the temperatures found on the various planets control the possibility that water will be found there in a liquid state, and thus set limits on its ability to support life. This point is discussed more exhaustively by E. W. Maunder in his book, *Are the Planets Inhabited?* We will return to it often as we proceed to examine the planets in later chapters.

2. The simplest way to attack the methods by which living matter is produced is to look at those organisms which are closest to us—men and animals. We do not create any organic materials whatever. We build up and maintain our vital substance solely from organic matter which has already been produced. This matter consists of carbohydrates, fats, and proteins, in which the processes of life have been at work when we receive them.

We acquire these materials by ingesting the substance of plants and other animals that feed on plants. In a world —no matter how abundantly supplied with game—containing no other living matter except animals and birds and fish, we could not survive. No matter what we eat, we are dependent ultimately for subsistence on plants.

Because of this dependence, such heterotrophic creatures as men and beasts are unusually sensitive to the conditions that govern their food supply. Suppose, for example, that all plant life were destroyed overnight by a sudden pestilence or a change of climate. Within a few weeks at most, all animal life would be extinct. First the plant-eating mammals would succumb, and then the carnivorous creatures among whom are ourselves, as soon as our stored supplies of food were exhausted. The carrion-eating vultures would be the last to go.

In contrast to these parasitic beings (which include all the higher orders of life on earth) are the autotrophs. Their prime virtue in the struggle for survival is that they can build up organic matter from inorganic materials, and thus maintain themselves. Without animals or fish or birds, plant life could still flourish indefinitely. Plants are, in effect, endowed with the power of creation, while we are only able to consume what has been created for us. In this paradox lies one clue to the sense of helplessness in man, leading him to the conviction that his being is dependent on a higher agency—on a Creator.

Foremost among those independent organisms that produce their own substance are the photoautotrophs, which accomplish the feat by photosynthesis with the help of sunlight. They include all chlorophyl-bearing plants. Also they include some very primitive "green" animals, such as the fresh-water protozoon, *euglena viridis.*

Photosynthesis is a reaction of carbon dioxide (CO_2) with water, in which carbohydrates are built up under the catalytic action of chlorophyl. Solar energy is used in the process, as exemplified in this chemical formula:

$$6\ CO_2 + 6\ H_2O + \text{light energy} \rightarrow C_6H_{12}O_6 + 6\ O_2$$

In simpler terms, this means that six molecules of carbon dioxide and six molecules of water are transformed, with the addition of light energy from the sun, into one molecule of glucose (sugar) and six molecules of oxygen.

The glucose so derived is organic matter. At the same time oxygen (O_2) is liberated. By the process of metabolism in the plant, proteins and fats are then formed from the carbohydrates.

In this way, each year more than a trillion tons of fresh organic matter are created by plants. On that basic material which they cannot produce, all other creatures—insects, fish, birds, animals, and men—maintain their life and pursue their physiological functions.

Since the photoautotrophs are dependent only on their physical environment, and not on other organisms, their existence is much more stable than that of the heterotrophs. They can be expected to appear long before conditions are suitable for higher orders of life—as they did on earth—and to survive for a long while after these higher orders are gone. As we have seen, if the photoautotrophs cannot support themselves, more complex forms of life must vanish almost immediately.

There is another type of autotroph which is able to build up and maintain its own substance from inert matter without the help of sunlight. This organism is found on earth only among certain bacteria. It derives energy from inorganic materials by oxidation—the same system of combustion by which rust is formed from iron—and uses it to produce organic compounds, especially carbohydrates.

This process is called chemosynthesis. Nitrogen bacteria, sulphur bacteria, methane bacteria, hydrogen bacteria, and iron bacteria all use this method to sustain themselves. Like plants, they are independent of any other organic matter; unlike plants, they do their work in the dark, independent of the sun's energy. However, they do need oxygen, the basic chemical of life for animals. They cannot produce this essential element from carbon dioxide, as plants do. Hence, they too are indirectly dependent on plants.

Unless free oxygen is present in the environment, chemosynthesis will not be available for the development of living matter. And free oxygen, as it happens, is one of the less abundant chemicals in the rest of our universe. In all probability it will be found only where plant life has released it from its natural union with carbon, hydrogen, and other elements.

3. Until now we have been considering the process by which living matter is produced. This building up of organic materials, is called by physiologists, anabolism. The object of the process is not simply to create fresh living substance for its own sake. It is created for the purpose of being transformed into energy—that is, into the various activities which are characteristic of life. This is another

process, known as catabolism. Together they comprise the whole complex of biological functions which go under the name of metabolism.

Matter and energy are never dissociated from each other. Indeed, they are only separate aspects of the same thing. Where energy is not apparent, in such inert substances as petroleum or rock, it still is potentially available. The chemical processes of nature are designed to convert this potential energy into the actual or kinetic energy employed in such overt activities as motion or heat.

In the anabolic process of building up living matter, substances which are either devoid of overt energy or possess only a small amount of it are transposed into highly complex substances containing a large amount of energy that is readily used. The additional force required for the transformation is supplied, as we have seen, by the sun. Thus the process is one of changing kinetic energy (sunlight) into chemical energy, which is stored in food.

In catabolism, the process is reversed. The complex substances are broken down again into simple substances with little or no overt energy, and, in the course of this transformation, energy is set free, to be used in the various body functions. Thus chemical energy is converted once more into kinetic energy as motion, heat, and so on.

It will be seen that the bulk of the energy engaged in both processes emanates from the sun. In effect, the whole system of metabolism is a method of transforming solar energy into the physical energy of living creatures. The inert materials on which plants feed are simply used as a medium in which the original energy is stored, conveyed, and made easily available for release in the body. After the energy has been extracted from them, they are discarded as inert materials again—in the form of water, carbon dioxide, urea, and other waste matter.

There are two ways in which food can be broken down by catabolism in a living organism to release energy. The first and simplest is by fermentation. In this chemical process a complex molecule is split into two less complex pieces. A well known example is the division of a single molecule of glucose into two molecules of lactic acid. It follows this formula:

$$C_6H_{12}O_6 \rightarrow 2\ C_3H_6O_3 + \text{energy}$$

The breaking down of the molecule into its basic elements is incomplete here, and so the gain of energy is relatively small.

We find this method of liberating energy in primitive organisms, such as yeast, and in those which have food at their disposal in such abundance that they can afford to make only partial use of the bounty. Among the representatives of this leisure class are intestinal parasites.

The other system of catabolism is by combustion, using oxygen as the agent. An example of this type is the conversion of glucose into carbon dioxide, water, and energy by this formula:

$$C_6H_{12}O_6 + 6\ O_2 \rightarrow 6\ CO_2 + 6\ H_2O + \text{energy}$$

Here it will be evident that we have the exact reverse of the anabolic formula with which we started. (See page 14.) The six molecules each of carbon dioxide and water, which were converted by the addition of solar energy into a molecule of glucose and six molecules of oxygen, have now been restored to their original condition, and the light energy of the sun has become animal energy. The process of metabolism is complete.

This is the most economical form of catabolism, because it releases the greatest amount of energy from the smallest consumption of matter. It is the main source of energy for all highly organized plants and animals, including men. As we have seen, it is simply an elaborate device to transform solar energy into the energy required for biological activity, using oxygen released in the first process as an agent for the second.

We might speculate a bit on this complicated mechanism, and ask whether plant-and-animal metabolism is necessarily the most efficient way to translate the sun's energy into activity of the sort that life displays. It is conceivable that life itself, in the form that we know it, is an extremely primitive means to accomplish an end which might be better achieved by some more direct method—one that is unknown to us.

The cosmos could be filled with kinetic activity devoted to the same purpose that we serve—whatever it is—and we would have no sign of it. For without oxygen, the key to living processes of our own type, such a supermetabolic system elsewhere in the universe could not be detected by any means we now have. It would follow laws and principles completely beyond our experience.

But this is, after all, mere speculation. The object of our study is to learn whether biological activity of a kind familiar to us may be possible on other planets. In the endeavor we have only the signs of biological oxidation to guide us. We shall return to this process of combustion later on, when we discuss oxygen as a necessity of life.

4. The way in which living organisms obtain their chemical reactions, in building, storing, and consuming energy, is primarily by respiration—that is, by exchanging gases between their own bodies and the milieu around them. The two gases most commonly used are carbon dioxide (CO_2) and oxygen (O_2).

Green plants require carbon dioxide to create carbohydrates by photosynthesis. They draw it from water or air. At the same time oxygen is liberated and "exhaled" into the outside atmosphere.

In the process of combustion, to release energy, plants and animals both require oxygen. They draw it from water or air. At the same time carbon dioxide is liberated and exhaled into the atmosphere outside.

The system is one of continual exchange in the simultaneous functions of producing and consuming energy. For our purpose it is useful to spend a few moments contemplating the methods by which this exchange is accomplished.

In the case of very small or primitive organisms, the outer surface of the body itself is a sufficient area for respiration. Such lowly plants and animals breathe through their skins. But, with increasing size and complexity, the outer surface becomes inadequate to provide the quantity of gas needed to support life. And so the body develops more surface by folding the tissue in localized areas.

Such folded respiratory areas are found in fish, for instance, in the form of gills. These are simply outward extensions of the inner tissue, with its rich blood supply. In most land-based animals, and in birds and insects, a still greater increase of the respiratory area is acquired by expanding the surface fold inward, as a sac inclosed within the body. Thus we achieve the lungs of vertebrate creatures and the tracheal system of insects.

True lungs are found in three separate stages of development. In the newt there is a simple sac. In the frog it is subdivided into separate spaces by inner walls. In the warm-blooded animals it becomes finally an elaborate structure of bladder-like air cells, presenting a vast surface to the inspired air. A man's lungs, for example, cover an area of 75 to 125 square yards. Laid out flat on the ground, they would provide space enough for a badminton court.

The tracheae of insects form a system of tubes that start at the skin, branching into smaller tubes, until they end between the body cells—or even inside them. Both lungs and tracheae enable the animal to keep air within its own body. This air differs materially in composition from the ambient air outside the body. It maintains a special environment of its own inside the organism—a sort of private internal atmosphere.

Plants also have developed a system of exchanging gas within the body, and they too maintain an internal atmosphere inside their leaves. This principle is of the greatest importance in enabling the organism to adapt itself in a new or inhospitable environment. It represents a kind of buffer zone between the ideal atmosphere in which the plant or animal might wish to live and the one in which it actually finds itself.

The internal atmosphere is a necessity for intensive gas exchange of the type required either for carbon-dioxide assimilation to produce energy or for biological oxidation to consume it. As an effective air-conditioning system, it makes existence easier for the organism under severe climatic conditions.

We shall concern ourselves with this phenomenon, too, in greater detail later on, when we come to ponder the possibility of vegetation existing under the exotic circumstances on Mars.

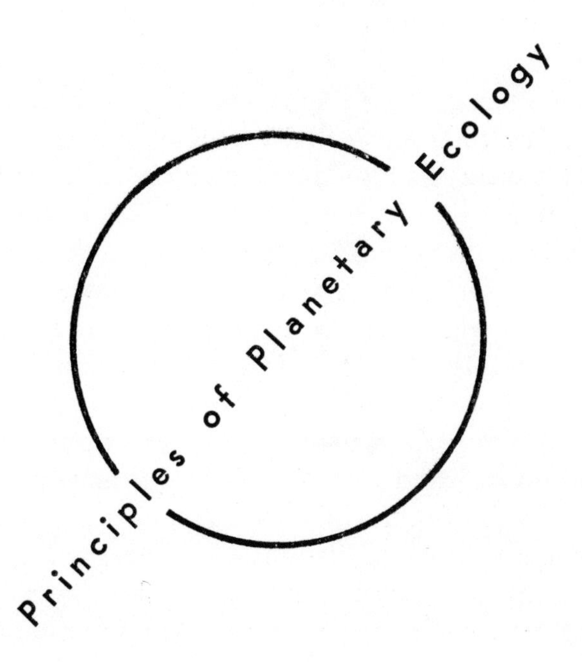

3

Study of the problem treated in this book is made considerably easier by the application of some well-established principles of ecology and physiology. As we have defined it earlier, an ecological space is one which permits living beings to exist in it, or one which is habitable for them. This characteristic implies that the space is provided with a well-balanced combination of conditions that make possible the existence of life and promote its development. Furthermore, the space must be free from factors that have a toxic effect on life and tend to destroy it.

Such a space may be considered both qualitatively and quantitatively favorable to life. But even though it may be free of biotoxic and biocidal factors, the space can become quantitatively unsuitable if the conditions friendly to life are present either in excess or in too low a degree. And so we come to a principle that plays a most important role in biology, and which will be a guiding rule in this study. It is the "principle of limiting factors," propounded by F. F. Blackman.

This principle is a further development of the "law of the minimum," first established by Justus von Liebig in 1849. In its simplest form, it states that environmental factors such as temperature, light, humidity, and the chemical constituents of soil, water, and air impose limits on life, if they are too great or abundant on the one hand, or if, on the other, they are too weak or sparse. A certain minimum must be attained, and a certain maximum must not be exceeded. Only within these limits can life exist and develop.

Between these two cardinal points—the minimum and the maximum—there lies also a third one. It is the optimum of an environmental condition, or of the environment which is a combination of such conditions; and it is distinguished by the fact that it is particularly favorable to the flourishing of life. (See Figure 1.) Impressive instances of this "law of the optimum" are found in the rubber states of the Far East and in the wheat belt on the North American continent.

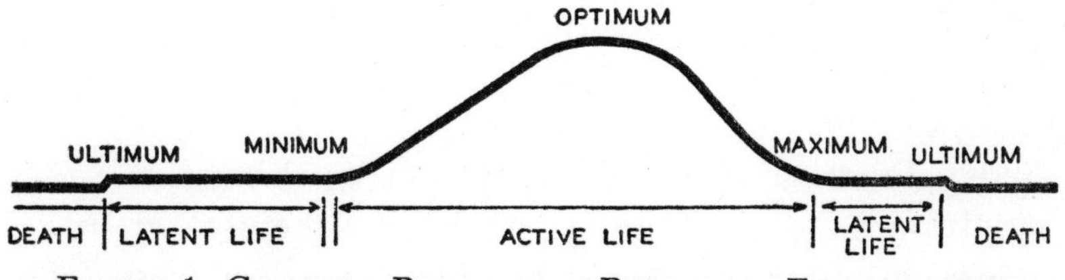

Figure 1. Cardinal Points of a Biological Environment

The space between the two limiting points indicates the range of active life, manifested by its growth, activity, and reproduction. Beyond the maximum and minimum, life does not generally succumb at once. Instead, it continues in the form of latent life, until it eventually terminates at the lethal limit. This point is known as the ultimum. It cannot be clearly defined in the lower range of latent life, because there is some doubt whether the total absence of any environmental factor necessarily inhibits life altogether. Too much is certainly fatal; too little may simply leave the organism in suspension.

Latent life sometimes is described by the terms, "resting state," "dormant stage," and "rigor." Thus we speak of a state of cold rigor, heat rigor, drought rigor, or hypoxia rigor (from lack of oxygen). We do not mean that, as in *rigor mortis,* life has fled from the organism so described. We mean only that too much or too little of the factor in question has suspended activity in the organism. A certain amount more (or possibly a certain amount less) would be required to bring it to the lethal point, where life itself—in any form that we can recognize—ceases.

The cardinal points of these environmental factors are by no means fixed and unalterable for a particular species or a specific life process. Rather, they can fluctuate widely in dependence on each other, and thus become "relatively limiting factors." If, for example, one such factor approaches the border line of the minimum, it may be compensated for by another factor which is situated nearer to the optimum.

Again, these cardinal points can be shifted at either end by reactions of the living beings themselves in response to their environment. Here we progress from simple physical ecology into the domain of physiological ecology, where life takes positive action to make itself more at home. A reaction of this sort may operate in such a way that life-supporting factors which are deficient will

FIGURE 2. SALAMANDER LARVAE

The salamander at left has been maintained in an oxygen-deficient environment; the one on the right in pure oxygen. After L. Dvastich, courtesy J. Springer.

become more readily available to the organism. This is a "useful" reaction. Or it may operate so that a loss of these factors is prevented. This is a "protective" reaction. All such responses, which serve to facilitate and defend the organism's existence, are called by the term, adaptation, or adjustment. Insofar as they involve morphological changes in the form of the organism itself, they are spoken of as morphoses.

A very impressive example of this kind is shown in Figure 2. The salamander at the left has lived in air that is low in oxygen; the one on the right in pure oxygen. The first shows an enlargement of the gills to such an extent that they hang outside the body in fringes, to increase the intake of oxygen. The effect of this adaptive mechanism is to compensate for the lack of oxygen in the animal's surroundings by enlarging the respiratory area. This means that the oxygen minimum has been shifted downward for that particular salamander. In addition to their increase in size, the cell walls of the gills have become thin and tender, so that they absorb the gas more easily. (See Figure 3.)

By way of contrast, the gills of the salamander living in pure oxygen (on the right in Figure 2) have become recessive to a noticeable extent; the cells have thickened to make absorption less easy. In this way the organism provides its own protection against the excessive concentration of oxygen.

Another well-known example is the increase of red blood cells and hemoglobin in animals adapted to high altitudes on the slopes of mountains. In the plant world it is observed that specimens which grow in shadow show a considerable enlargement of their leaves, in order to absorb as much light as possible. A case of protective adaptation against radiation is the thickening of the epi-

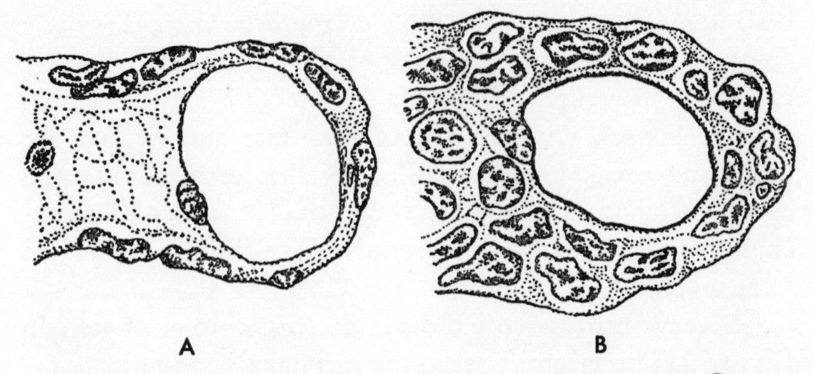

FIGURE 3. MICROSCOPIC SECTIONS THROUGH SALAMANDER GILLS

These sections through the threads of two salamander larvae's gills show: (A) cell walls of the animal maintained in an oxygen-deficient environment are thin and tender, to absorb more oxygen; while (B) those of the animal kept in pure oxygen have become thicker, for protection against too much oxygen. Redrawn after L. Dvastich, courtesy J. Springer.

dermis in animals and people exposed for prolonged periods to sunlight, and the development of pigments in leaves.

Thus the laws of the minimum, of limiting factors, and of the optimum, all are connected intimately with the adaptive responses of the organism. Their close relationship gives us an insight into the range of tolerance of living creatures toward their environment.

This range of tolerance varies widely in different organisms. Where it is very broad the plant or animal is labeled eurykous; where the range is very narrow it is called stenokous. Euryky and stenoky can also be applied to a single biophilic factor. In the case of temperature, one speaks of eurythermal and stenothermal organisms. The eurythermal can endure great contrasts of heat and cold; the stenothermal cannot. There are lower plants (lichens, for instance) which are capable of standing temperature variations of about 180 degrees Fahrenheit. Also there are sensitive tropical plants whose range of tolerance is little more than 20 degrees.

These phenomena of living matter are the basis of physical and physiological ecology. They must be realized thoroughly and applied in attacking the problem of the possibility of life under conditions such as are found on other planets.

It is not the aim of this book to examine all the ecological qualities of all the planets. No such exhaustive study of their environmental conditions is necessary. Instead, we can approach the problem much more simply by taking one dominant factor at the start. That one is temperature. By means of this yardstick, certain planetary atmospheres can be excluded altogether as possible ecospheres for living things.

To those that remain, after this overall ecological survey of the planets, we can apply another limiting factor—the oxygen content of the atmosphere. This particular characteristic is chosen because oxygen, as we have seen, is an essential element in any environment if it is to support life as we know it. Also it is a handy means of classifying organic matter, separating it into oxibiotic and anoxibiotic organisms—those that do and those that do not draw oxygen directly from the air or from the water.

This method of examining the subject "by exclusion," as philosophers put it, seems to me to bring us by the shortest route to the heart of our problem. After showing that life on certain planets is evidently *not* possible, and after screening the various kinds of organic life in the light of what is known about the others, we should be left with a reasonably clear picture of what *is* possible.

In point of fact, we shall find that we are left with Mars as the one planet, outside of our own and possibly Venus, on which considerations of temperature do not rule out the suspicion of life in some familiar form. We find that oxygen is present on Mars—if at all—only in minute quantities: another reason for taking oxygen as our final standard of exclusion. And so, by this method, we are brought back to the basic subject of this book, the "green and red planet," and to the practical question of the kinds of life we might expect to find there.

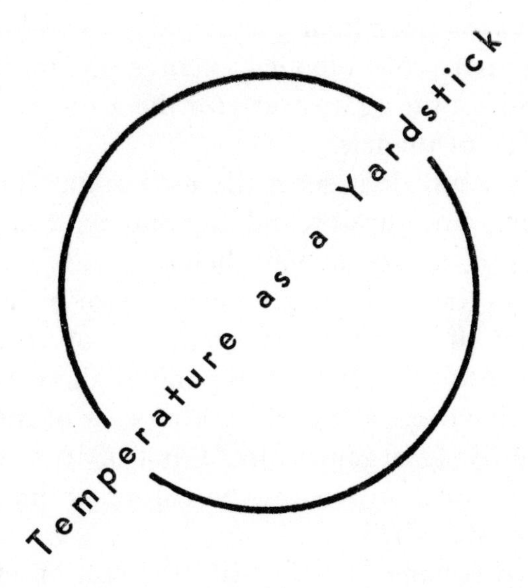

4

Perhaps the most decisive factor in establishing a suitable environment for life is temperature. This fact has been impressed upon the face of our earth in a striking manner. It is temperature that imposes limits on the geographical distribution of plants and animals, human settlement, civilization, and culture.

It was temperature that determined the ecological level in our geological eras, ranging from the extreme of luxuriant vegetation in the warm intervals to the barren extreme of the glacial epochs. In biology, body temperature is used as an accurate means of classifying organisms: they are either homoiothermal (warm-blooded) or poikilothermal (cold-blooded) beings. Temperature likewise provides a fitting measure for the ecological qualities of the different planets.

The Kelvin scale is generally used to measure absolute temperatures in physics and astronomy. Starting with absolute zero, at about 460° below zero Fahrenheit, it ranges up to the equivalent of nearly two billion degrees Fahrenheit. In all this vast gradation of temperatures, shown in Figure 4, only a small band of about 110 degrees permits active life. (We are speaking now of the temperature of the living organism itself, not of its environment. The surrounding milieu can be colder or hotter within fairly narrow limits.)

Below this band of active life the motion of its molecules slows down, until they come to rest completely at absolute zero. Above this band the molecules break up, by thermal dissociation, and become other kinds of matter. Beyond about 5,000° F the shells of the atoms begin to crack, as a result of thermal ionization. Above 20 to 35 million degrees F the heat affects even the nucleus of the atom. Thus only a brief octave on the immense scale of temperatures found in the universe provides the relatively stable environment required for active life.

Now let's consider this zone and its environs in more detail. The range within which the functions of active life—growth, metabolism, movement, reproduction, and so on—are possible starts a few degrees below the freezing point of water, and it reaches up to about 140° F. The

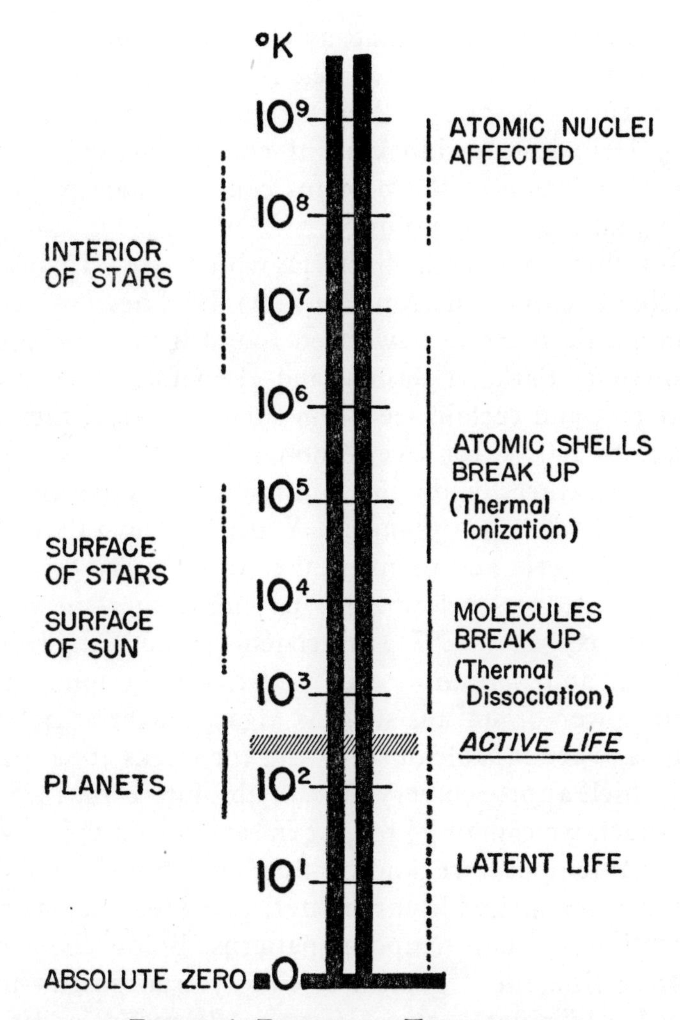

FIGURE 4. EFFECTS OF TEMPERATURE

This diagram uses the Kelvin scale, which is calibrated in centigrade degrees above absolute zero (—273° C). Note that it is shown here as increasing by logarithmic steps: 10^1 equals 10° K, 10^2 equals 100° K, and so on. This makes it possible to present the whole range of temperatures in such a way that the band of active life—an infinitesimal part of it—will be visible at all. On an ordinary arithmetical scale the 61 degrees centigrade that permit active life would make a line so thin (about 1/30,000,000 of an inch) that it could not even be seen.

band of temperatures that are suitable for life thus amounts to roughly 110 degrees. Above this zone, living matter enters a state of "heat rigor," in physiological terms. Dehydration, blocking of enzyme action, and finally coagulation of the proteins constitute the probable course that leads to dissolution.

But there are some bacteria which are capable of growth at temperatures up to 170° F. These so-called thermophilic bacteria have been found in hot springs in Yellowstone Park, in Bosnia, and elsewhere. The spores of bacteria and certain seeds can survive even if they are exposed to 250° F for several hours.

Temperatures below the minimum for active life are soon lethal for most organisms. Yet it is known that trees in North Siberia and plants in the Arctic survive cold as low as 75 degrees below zero. By immersing specimens in liquid oxygen (−297°), nitrogen (−320°), hydrogen (−422°), and helium (−452°) it has been found that certain lower organisms such as algae, bacteria, lichens, and mosses are capable of surviving for weeks at temperatures which approach very near to absolute zero.

In fact, we cannot go too far in saying that there is no depth of temperature known that is definitely able to destroy every sort of living matter, provided the onset of cold follows certain temporal patterns. Below the range of active life, the organism is simply transposed—in a state of cold rigor—into a latent or dormant condition. It is this suggestion, found in the work of Luyet and Gehenio (see the Bibliography), that leads the physiologist to suspect that life could survive the extreme cold of space, to appear and develop at the proper time on other planets.

Indeed, it is interesting to note that these recent findings, which were unknown forty years ago, cast a new and encouraging light on the suggestion of Svante Arrhenius and others that life could have arrived on earth by way of the meteors which constantly invade our air. If living organisms could survive the extreme cold of space, there is no reason why they could not be distributed throughout the universe in this way, to flourish wherever the environment is favorable.

From this rough sketch of the thermal limits of life in its active phase, we can now orient ourselves as we examine the question: Which planets in their present state of development permit life, and which do not? By superimposing the temperature scale of life on the range of planetary temperatures, we find that only the earth covers the entire band of active life. Its normal temperatures run from about 75 degrees below zero F to nearly 140 degrees above. The zone of active life lies within the upper half of this scale, which covers more than 215 degrees. In its lower half it reaches down into the zone of latent life. (See Figure 5.)

On Mars the temperature range is from 95 degrees below zero to about 85 above. In its upper quarter it coincides with the lower half of the biothermal band. Like the earth's—but even more deeply—it reaches downward into the region of latent life.

Venus includes the entire band of active life within the temperatures found in various layers of its atmosphere.

But Mercury's heat extends far beyond the highest point on the scale of biotemperatures. Its environment is in the lethal range for living matter.

At the other end of the scale, the outer planets of our solar system lie deep in the chill range of latent life. From Jupiter (−240° F) through Saturn, Uranus, and Neptune out to Pluto (−380°), they vary between 275 and 410 degrees below the minimum for biological activity.

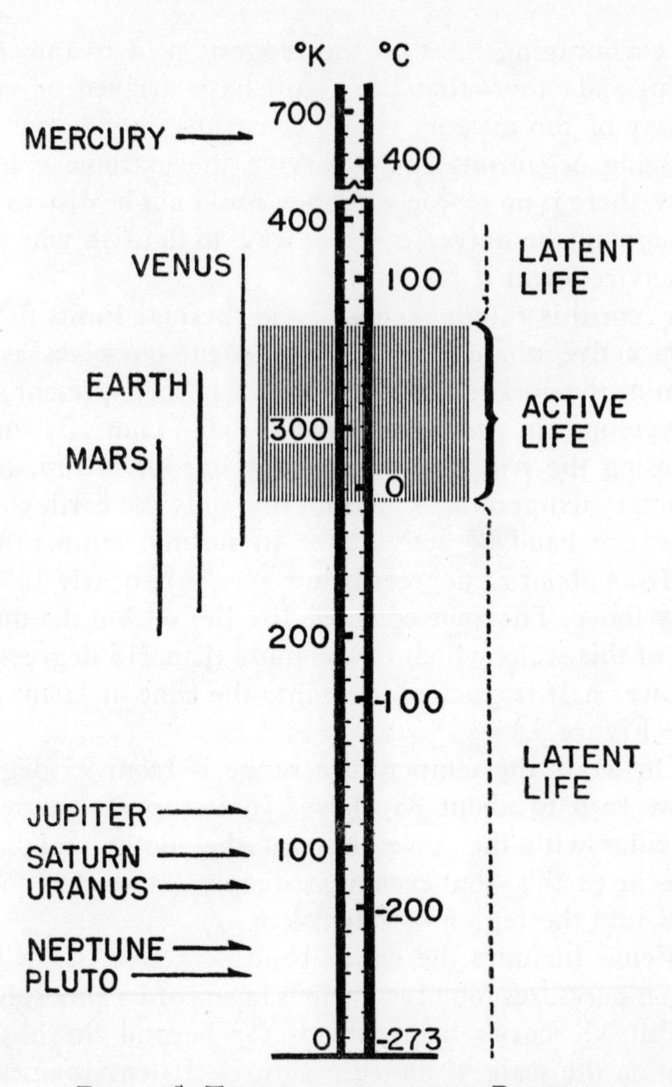

FIGURE 5. TEMPERATURES OF THE PLANETS

Here the range of temperatures on the various planets of our solar system (left side of the diagram) is related to the bands of active and latent life (on the right). It is seen that only Venus, the earth, and Mars lie within the part of the range that will support biological activity.

It may be added that the temperature of the Moon fluctuates violently between a low of 240 degrees below zero F at night and a high of 212 degrees above—the boiling point of water on our planet—in the daytime. At both extremes it is insupportable for active life.

It follows, then, that from the standpoint of temperature alone Mars and perhaps Venus* are the only planets, aside from the earth, which at present possess the prerequisites for living matter as we know it. All the other planets are excluded, for their temperatures lie far outside the range of active life.

It is worth noting that the three planets which are thermally favorable to life all move in neighboring orbits from 67,000,000 miles (in the case of Venus) to 142,000,000 miles (in the case of Mars) mean distance from the sun. The earth is nearly in the middle of this band, with an orbit whose mean radius is 93,000,000 miles.

The distance from the sun is a decisive factor for the temperatures of the planets, and therefore for the possibility of life on them. The intensity of any radiation decreases with the inverse square of its distance from the source. A convenient figure used by physicists to measure the sun's heat on a planet is derived from a formula known as the "solar constant." It is radiation expressed in calories per unit of area for a specific time. At the top of the earth's atmosphere the solar constant is 1.92 calories per square centimeter per minute.

A calorie, in this sense, is the amount of heat required to raise a gram of water—about one-thirtieth of an ounce

* In a conversation with the author, Dr. Heinz Haber, now of the University of California at Los Angeles, has suggested that a primitive kind of life might be found on Venus in the form of a biological aerosol, drifting in certain strata of the planet's atmosphere. See footnote, page 132, *The Journal of Aviation Medicine,* April 1952.

—exactly one degree Centigrade (or 1.8° F) under the atmospheric pressure found at sea level. In an hour and forty minutes this amount of heat would bring a gram of water from freezing to the boiling point. Now, if the metric formula is translated into familiar terms, it means that the earth receives each minute enough sunlight on each square inch of area at the top of the atmosphere to raise nearly half an ounce of water one degree Centigrade—or enough on each square foot to bring almost a half-gallon of frozen water to a boil in one hundred minutes. This is the heat which, converted into other kinds of energy, provides the motive power for all the activities of living things on this planet.

Two points must be remembered about this figure. One is that it applies only under the pressure found at sea level—and of course no pressure at all exists at the top of the atmosphere. The other is that the depth and character of the atmosphere itself will affect the amount of this heat that filters down to the solid ground underneath. The quantity of heat that reaches the surface of the earth, for example, is something less than half the solar constant—enough on each square foot, let's say, to boil three pints of frozen water in an hour and forty-five minutes. On the moon, which has no appreciable atmosphere, the solar constant as a measure of heat would be valid at the surface of the ground. On the other hand, the fact that there is almost no atmospheric pressure on the Moon would make it impossible for water to exist at all in a liquid state.

On other planets which have atmospheres, such as Mars, we do not know exactly what conditions affect the amount of heat transmitted to the surface. In some cases—because the atmosphere is thinner or reflects less heat—the proportion may be greater than on earth. Neverthe-

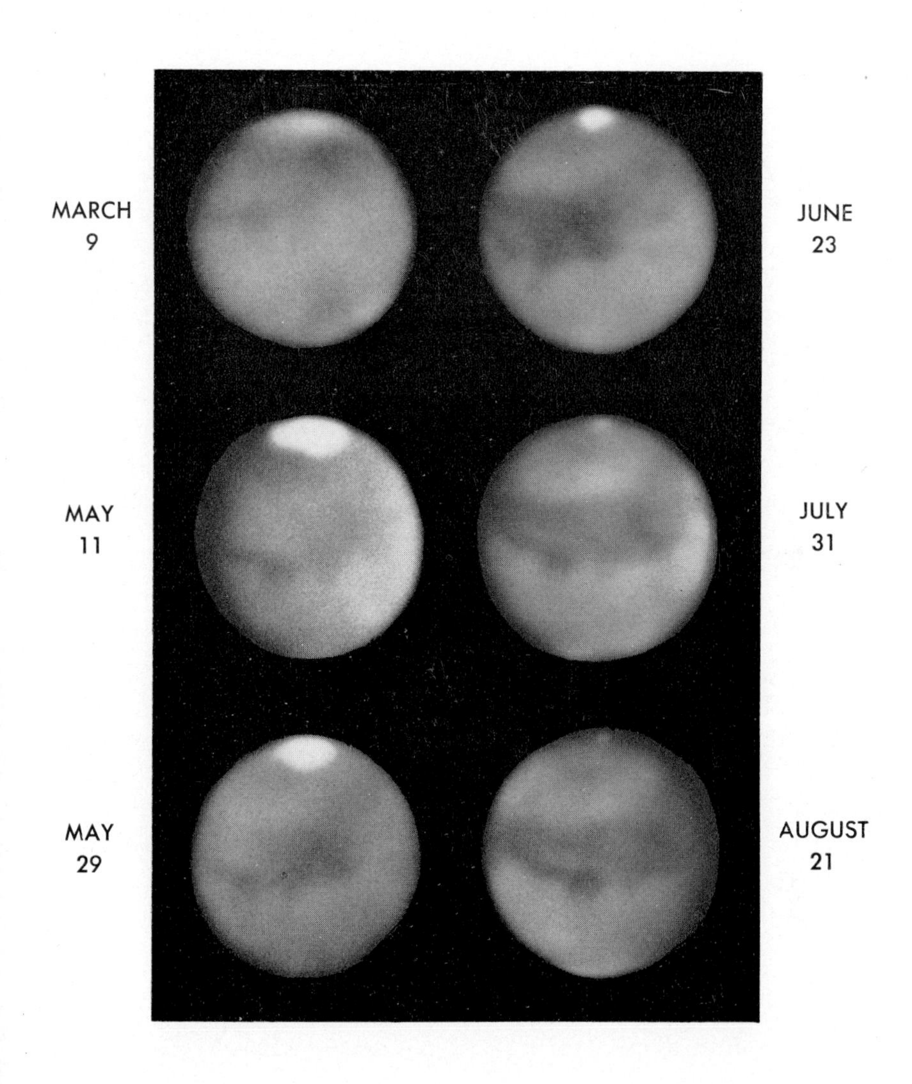

PLATE I. MARS AT DIFFERENT SEASONS

These photographs show the melting of the south (top) polar snow cap and the darkening of the tropics during the Martian summer. The dates given are Martian seasonal dates, as they would correspond to those on the earth. Photographs by E. C. Slipher, Lowell Observatory.

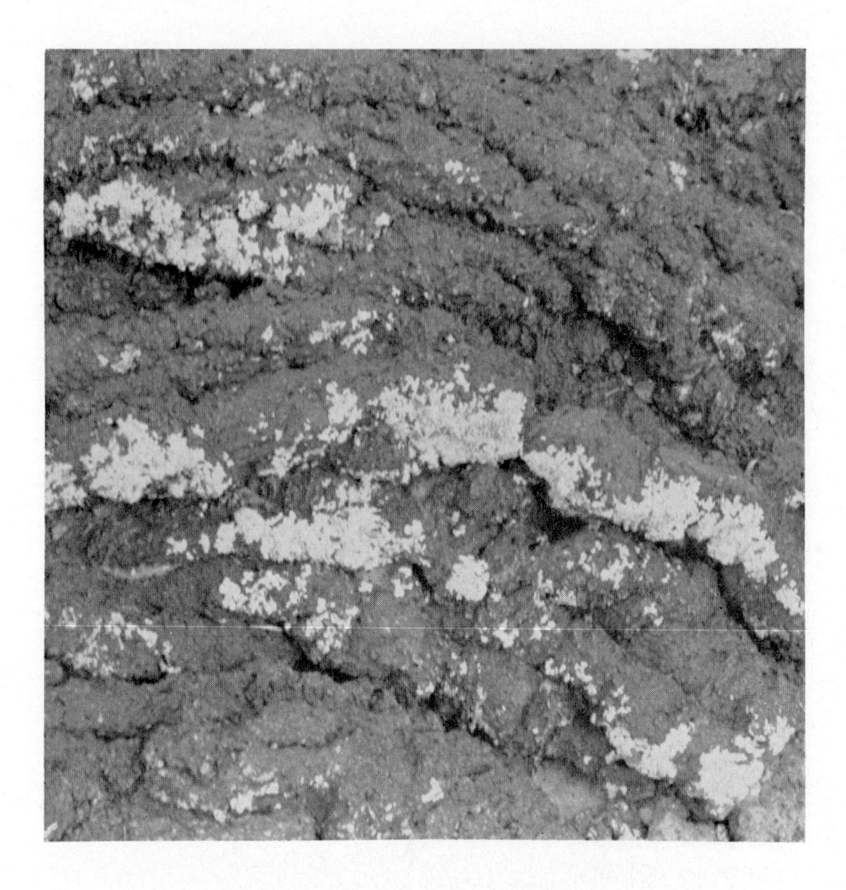

PLATE II. A LAVA BED WITH LICHENS

A bed of lava on an extinct volcano near Carrizozo, New Mexico, shows how life may start. The lichens growing on the barren mass will break it down in time, and pave the way for more complex plants.

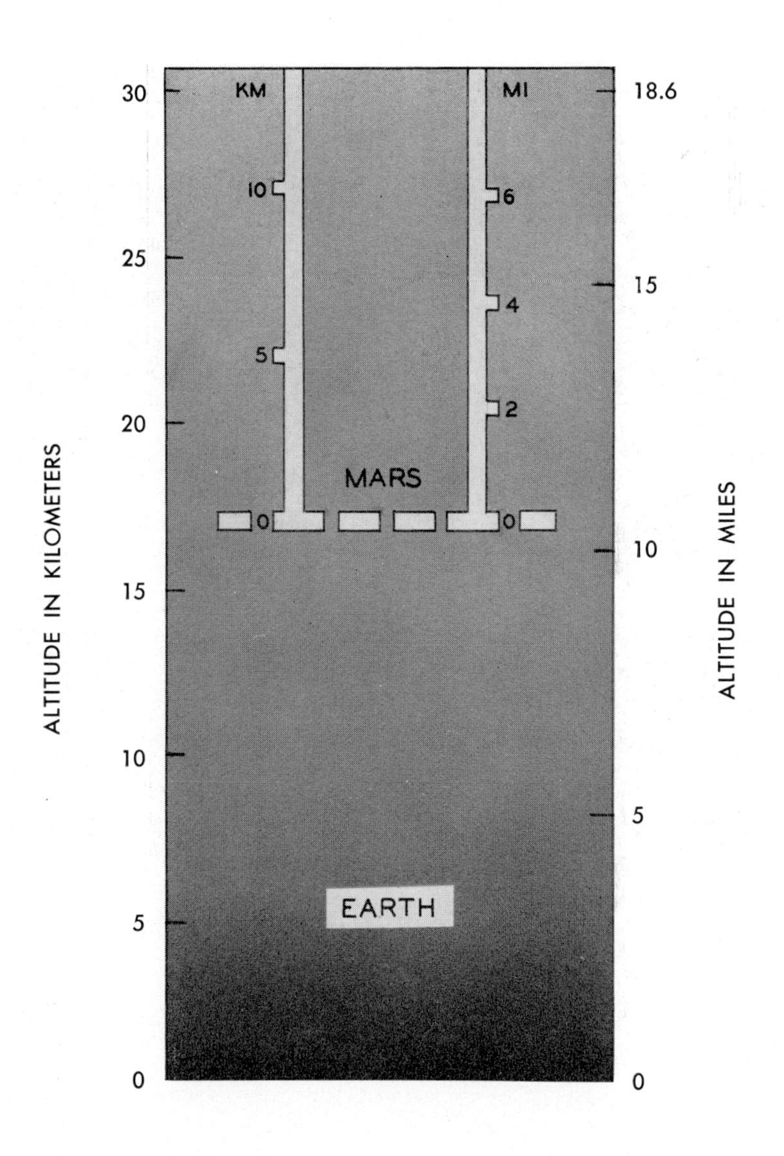

PLATE III. THE ATMOSPHERES OF MARS AND THE EARTH

The atmosphere of Mars is superimposed on that of the earth at an equivalent altitude of about eleven miles. At this level, corresponding to the surface of Mars, they are the same. But above this height the density of the Martian air decreases less rapidly than that of the earth, because of the weaker gravitational force acting on its molecules.

Plate IV. A Candle Flame at Various Altitudes

A candle flame grows steadily more feeble as it "ascends" in a low-pressure chamber to a height of eleven miles. The reason for this is an increasing lack of the oxygen it requires for fuel. Above this altitude —and on the surface of Mars—a candle will not burn.

less, the solar constant is useful as a comparative measure of the warmth available to a planet from the sun. And on Mars the solar constant is only 0.84 calories per square centimeter per minute, less than half that of the earth.

This means that at the top of the Martian atmosphere —sixty miles up, as compared to the 300-mile depth of our own air—only enough heat is available from the sun to boil about a fifth of a gallon of water in the time that it takes us to boil our half gallon. Even though Mars may receive proportionately more of this warmth on its surface than we do on ours, the probability is that the thermal range on Mars is considerably lower than on earth. And this assumption is confirmed by careful observations of the temperatures on Mars' surface.

The corresponding thermal values for Mercury and Venus, in calories per square centimeter per minute, are shown in Figure 6. From this chart we can deduce that the intensity of radiation that Mercury receives is more than six times that of the earth. For Venus it is nearly twice as much. As we have seen, the solar constant for Mars is less than half our own, and that of Jupiter is about one twenty-fifth. Pluto, the outermost of our planets, is forty times more distant from the sun than the earth; and it receives, on an average, only one sixteen-hundredth as much heat and light per unit of area as we do.

Even so, when Pluto is at its closest to the sun (2.75 billion miles) that majestic body appears as large as Venus does to us, and many times more brilliant. It is then a star of the −19 magnitude, giving some 600 times as much light as we receive from the Moon. During the "day" on Pluto it would provide a sort of dim and eerie radiance—comparable to that which illumines our world when all but a thin crescent of the sun is in eclipse—

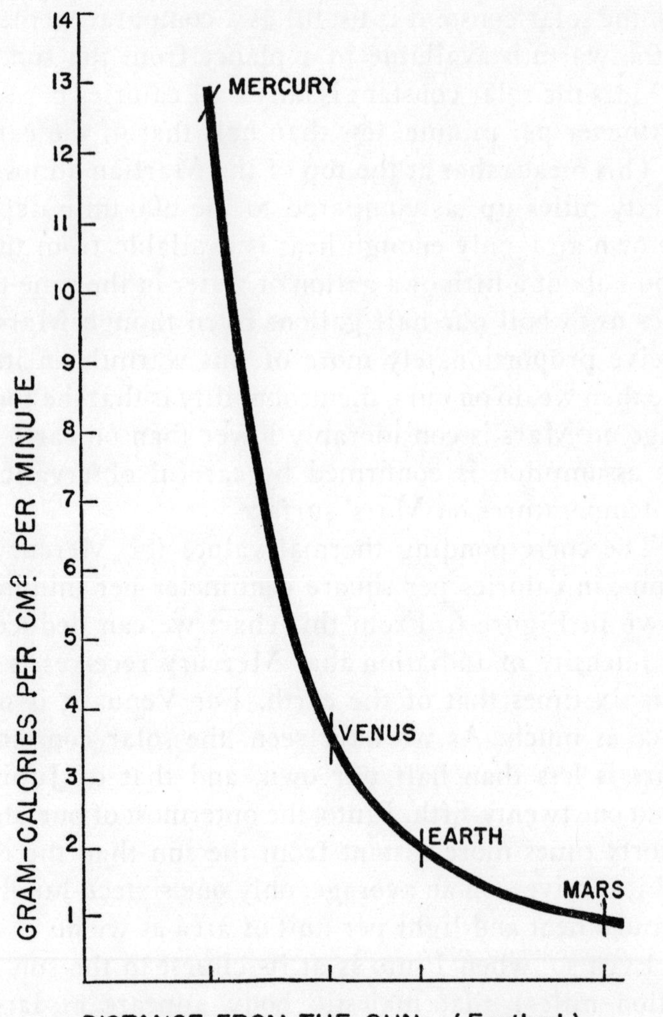

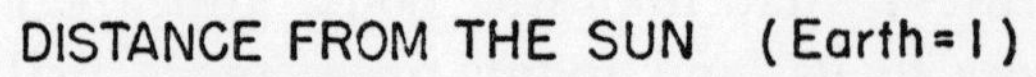

FIGURE 6. SOLAR CONSTANTS OF CERTAIN PLANETS

The amount of solar radiation available to the planets from Mercury to Mars is shown on the vertical scale in calories per square centimeter per minute.

through which the other stars would continue to shine as at night.

Indeed, it is doubtful whether living creatures on Pluto, if there could be any, would ever realize the peculiar relationship of their home to this star. It would exert no appreciable effect upon their weather or their seasons. If they noticed its steady course across the sky, as opposed to the more complex movements of the rest, they would perhaps remark on it as an interesting phenomenon—like the fixed station of Polaris in our sky—but as one of no obvious significance to themselves.

They would no doubt take it for granted that Pluto is the center of the universe, as most inhabitants of the earth assumed of our own planet before Copernicus, and there would be a good deal more reason in their assumption. The 248 years that it takes Pluto to revolve around the sun would contribute to this delusion. For if the other objects in the heavens exercised no visible influence on their daily lives, there would be no occasion to look upon them with more than idle curiosity, and the science of astronomy would not evolve.

But that's a digression. To sum up what we have found: Mercury is too near the intense heat of the sun to bear active life; while the outer planets (even though the sun still presents to them a spectacle of startling brilliance) are too far away. Only a small zone about 75 million miles wide—out of the 4,300 million that stretch between the sun and Pluto at its farthest point—provides a planetary environment well-suited to the existence of life. We might call this zone the thermal ecosphere of the sun.

Other stars may have such ecospheres of their own, with planets in them that are capable of supporting life similar to ours. But the nearest of those stars—Alpha

Centauri—is almost 26 trillion miles away. It is too far for us to see, even with the most powerful telescope, whether or not it has any planets revolving about it. Only the most delicate calculations, based on deviations in the motions of the stars revealed by the spectroscope, give any hope of some day detecting the existence of a few large planets circling the closest of our cosmic neighbors.

Supposing that we had a space ship capable of accelerating up to nearly 186,000 miles a second—the highest theoretical speed attainable by any object in the physical universe—and then decelerating again on a journey to that star, it would take a round trip of more than seventeen years* to visit Alpha Centauri. So it is more than possible that we may never know the answer to the most basic question about our sun's closest neighbor in space: whether it has planets on which life could exist. That is why this book confines itself to the likelihood of some form of life on other planets in our own solar system.

Even in our own solar system, some terrestrial bodies such as Pluto and Titan—one of Saturn's moons, which is nearly the size of Mars—are so small and remote that we have the utmost difficulty establishing the most elementary facts about them. Using instruments of extraordinary delicacy, Gerard P. Kuiper has so far been unable to secure more than a tentative figure for the mass and radius of Pluto or the composition of Titan's atmosphere.

It should be added that there are several other factors besides its distance from the sun that affect the temperature of a planet's atmosphere. These include the planet's mass, its stage of development, its period of rotation,

* By the foreshortening of time at speeds approaching light, predicated in Einstein's theory, the duration of the voyage would be somewhat less for the travelers themselves under these ideal conditions: roughly about thirteen years. But that too would seem an impossibly long journey in the narrow confines of a space ship, which must carry its own oxygen, food, and enormous quantities of fuel to maintain its acceleration and deceleration.

radioactivity within it, and especially the composition of its atmosphere, if it has one.

Conceivably there might be local temperature conditions on some of the outer planets or their satellites that would make a form of life possible. The present state of our knowledge makes any such possibility seem highly remote. In any case, the sun's distance is the primary consideration—particularly on the nearer planets which we know reasonably well. And so we have used this factor to rule out those planets which, in the best judgment of a physiologist at the present time, could not support life in any familiar form.

The two that remain then are Venus and Mars. I do not propose to examine Venus here in any detail, for several reasons. One is that this survey of the other planets is intended only for background, to place Mars in its proper perspective as a possible scene of active life. The main reason is, however, that virtually nothing is known about the surface of Venus or its fitness as a biological habitation, even though it is our closest neighbor after the Moon.

The enigmatic face of Venus is caused by an atmosphere so dense that we cannot be sure what is underneath it. The actual dimensions of the planet, as a solid sphere, are uncertain. We judge that the depth of its atmosphere is comparable to our own, but we do not know. All we are able to view is the outer layer, a brilliant, opaque mask that conceals the physical features down below.

Hence a detail so simple as the length of the day on Venus—which would affect the character of its climate—is still a mystery. Its rotation is generally assumed to be slower than ours. Estimates have ranged from about ten of our days to 225 days, the length of the year on Venus. If the longer figure were true, Venus would, like

Mercury, present the same side constantly to the sun. Its surface temperature has been calculated at more than 120° F, with a range up to 140° at midday in the tropics. This of course would not rule out the possibility of life under certain conditions in more temperate latitudes.

But the main objection to life on Venus is that it appears to have neither water nor oxygen in its atmosphere. Without one or both of these constituents, biological activity would be inconceivable by any laws we know. The only gas of biological significance that has been detected so far in the air of Venus is carbon dioxide in enormous quantities.

So we are compelled to lay aside the possibility of life on Venus for the present, and turn our attention once more to Mars. The green and red planet, though it is farther away from us than Venus, has a much thinner atmosphere. We are able to see through it with comparative ease, so that we can observe and measure many of the features on its surface.

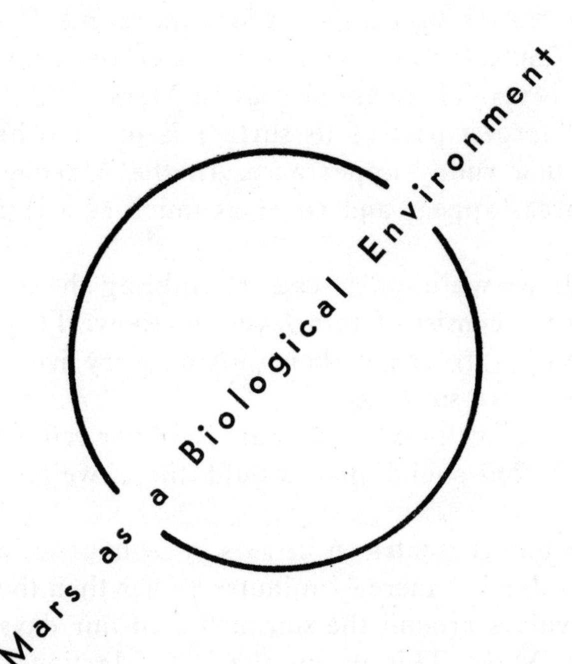

5

Before we proceed with our biological examination of Mars, let us glance briefly over some of the astronomical data and other pertinent facts about the planet. These facts and figures will supply the basis for our discussion.

The mean diameter of Mars is 4,250 miles. That of the earth is 7,913 miles, or nearly twice as great.

Its surface area is 52,500,000 square miles. The earth's is 196,950,000 square miles—four times as much. But only about 57,500,000 square miles of the earth's area is land; the rest is sea. There are no seas on Mars.

The largest part of its surface is of an ochre color, giving it a ruddy appearance. In the Martian spring, green areas appear and cover as much as a third of its surface.

It shows white polar caps resembling those of earth. These caps consist of thin layers of snow. They are not composed of frozen carbon dioxide (dry ice) as some observers once supposed.

The surface gravity on Mars is 38 per cent of that on earth. A 200-pound man would there weigh only 76 pounds.

The planet rotates on its axis in 24 hours 37 minutes. Thus its day is a mere 41 minutes longer than the earth's.

It revolves around the sun in 687 of our days, or 668 days on Mars. This means that the Martian year and seasons are nearly twice the length of ours.

The mean distance of Mars from the sun is 141,710,000 miles. This compares with 93,000,000 miles, the distance of the earth from the sun.

Its orbital velocity is 15 miles per second. The earth's is 18.5 miles per second.

The atmosphere of Mars has a depth of 60 miles. That of the earth is 300 miles deep.

Its probable barometric pressure is 60 to 70 millimeters of mercury on the surface. At sea level the earth's barometric pressure is 760 millimeters of mercury. (Here we come to a measure of atmospheric pressures which has not been mentioned before in this book. It will be explained presently.)

The main chemical constituents of the Martian atmosphere may well be nitrogen and argon. The main constituents of our own are nitrogen and oxygen.

The proportion of carbon dioxide in the atmosphere is probably greater than on earth.

Oxygen so far has not been detected in the air of Mars.

Water vapor is present, but in very small amounts.

The temperature may reach 85° F above the green areas in the tropics at noon. During the night it drops as low as −95° F. (See Figure 7.)

With these physical facts about Mars in mind, let us now turn back for a moment to the discussion of temperature as an ecological yardstick (Chapter 4). We found that the daily temperature on Mars varies by as much as 180 degrees. This is many times the normal daily variation on earth. In addition, the whole temperature band of Mars is in a range from 20 to 40 degrees lower than ours. If living things should exist on Mars, they would have to be able to withstand such rigorous changes of temperature not merely from season to season, as we do, but from hour to hour.

In this connection it is worth noting that the coldest natural temperature ever recorded on earth was 90° below zero at the Siberian village of Yerkhoyansk in 1892. This is only 5 degrees less than the coldest extreme on Mars. The hottest temperature ever recorded on earth was 136° near Tripoli in 1922. Thus there is a variation of at least 225 degrees in inhabited areas of the earth—though not in the same areas at the same time of year, as is the case on Mars.

A point of interest too is that the Martian climate, while it is subject to greater extremes of heat and cold than ours in the course of a single 24-hour period, is also much more equable than ours. That is, it does not give way to sudden storms and violent changes of temperature

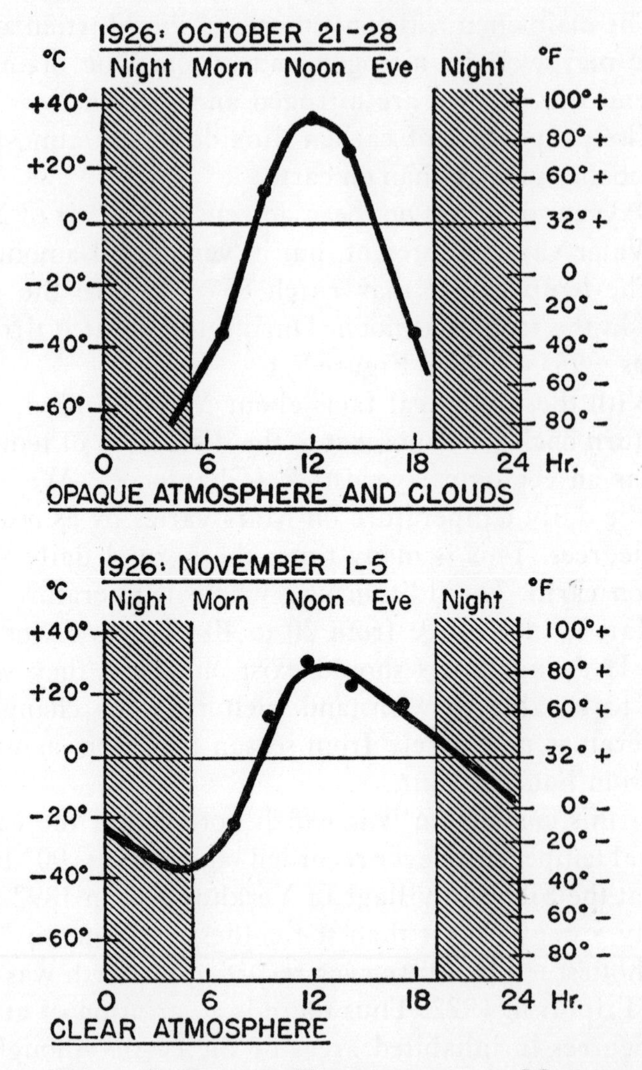

FIGURE 7. DIURNAL TEMPERATURES ON MARS

Variations in the daily temperature of Mars are shown for the southern tropical region near to midsummer in the southern hemisphere. These radiometric measurements were made by W. W. Coblentz at the Lowell Observatory in 1926. After G. de Vaucouleurs, courtesy Faber and Faber.

to the extent that the earth's climate does. This is primarily because the surface of Mars shows less variation than that of the earth. There are no large bodies of water, for instance, and no mountains apparently of any great size or startling configuration. Mars seems to be, on the whole, a body of land showing the same composition at the same general altitude.

On the earth we divide living beings into two categories, according to the behavior of their body temperature with relation to the temperature of their environment. These are, as we have noted, the poikilothermal and the homoiothermal—in popular terminology, the "cold blooded" and the "warm blooded."

In the poikilothermal type, embracing plants and animals up to and including reptiles, body temperature is dependent directly on environmental temperature. They thrive on warmth, and become torpid when the temperature falls.

In the homoiothermal type, embracing birds and mammals (including men), body temperature is independent of the ambient temperature outside. Their thermal constancy is maintained by a physical and chemical mechanism which regulates their temperature. This chemical thermostat requires a relatively high metabolism, to generate heat. Hence, warm-blooded creatures need much more oxygen than cold-blooded creatures, for the heat energy demanded by the highly-organized homoiothermal type can be gained—so far as we know—only through the process of biological oxidation discussed in Chapter 2.

So the temperature factor now leads us to another important environmental quality which is closely connected with it. This factor is oxygen. On its presence or absence —and on its amount—hangs the possibility or not of life on Mars, and the particular kind of life which might be found.

In the same way that we used the factor of temperature in the previous chapter, to screen the various planets with regard to their hospitality to living matter, let us now use the factor of oxygen to screen the environment of Mars for those types of matter which may and may not exist there. Along with oxygen we can include some other ecological conditions, such as light, water, and carbon dioxide. The last of these is significant mainly in discussing the possibility of vegetation.

The great significance of oxygen as a necessity of life was recognized soon after its discovery in 1796. It was called "the substance of life" by the great French physicist, Antoine Lavoisier. Its claim to this title comes from the fact that living matter (its water included) consists up to 60 per cent of oxygen. More than that, oxygen is one of the agents in the most important of all chemical reactions for living organisms: biological oxidation, which releases energy.

Another way of converting matter into energy without oxygen, as we have seen, is by fermentation—splitting the food molecules into smaller particles. Sometimes called anaerobic respiration, because it doesn't require air, this method is far less efficient than combustion by the use of oxygen. Only the most primitive organisms use it, and there is no conceivable way in which it could be developed to meet the large energy requirements of the higher orders of life. The one means known to satisfy these requirements is through aerobic respiration, using oxygen.

Aerobic respiration demands a fairly high concentration of oxygen in the medium—air or water—surrounding the organism. In the altitudes at which most organisms live on earth, this concentration amounts to about 90 quintillion (that is 9×10^{18} or 90 followed by eighteen more zeros) molecules of oxygen in each cubic inch of air. If the concentration is much less, the organism soon begins to suffer from hypoxia. This causes physiological disturbances, and eventually brings the biological functions to a standstill.

Thus oxygen is one of the most important conditions of an ecological environment. If a certain O_2 minimum is not found, the combination of circumstances favorable to life shows a noticeable gap. This lack, by itself, excludes a large class of living things.

Such a lack exists on Mars. According to careful measurements by Adams and Dunham (see Bibliography) and more recently by Kuiper, oxygen cannot be detected in the Martian atmosphere. Either it is not there at all or it is present only in minute traces.

Now, if the situation is as it appears on that planet, it is relatively simple to answer the question whether higher types of living beings, as we know them, could exist on Mars. But since "the little men from Mars" have received so much attention in the press lately, in connection with the so-called flying saucers, we should perhaps examine the question comprehensively, and show—step by step—what living creatures can definitely be excluded from discussion on Mars, merely by the absence of oxygen in sufficient quantity.

First let us have a look at the oxygen minimum which is barely sufficient for the vital activities of living organisms at various levels of development. We find a great deal of research on this point in the literature of physiology and aviation medicine. In tracking down the answer to the question, laboratory experiments have been tried with various mixtures of oxygen and nitrogen, with thin air in low-pressure chambers, and with water from which the gas content has been removed.

Here it is convenient to explain that physiologists and meteorologists everywhere measure atmospheric pressure with a mercury barometer, calibrated in millimeters rather than inches or degrees. At sea level on the earth the total atmospheric pressure is 760 mm of mercury, the symbol of which is Hg. As you go up, the pressure falls: at 5,000 feet it is only 632 mm Hg, at 15,000 feet it drops to 429 mm Hg, and so on until at 160,000 feet (or 30 miles) the pressure is less than 1 mm Hg.

The oxygen content of our air is about 21 per cent of the total pressure, or 160 mm Hg at sea level. It maintains almost a constant proportion at all altitudes up to 50 miles or so. Hence, the O_2 pressure can always be calculated from the total atmospheric pressure for any height at which the amount of oxygen in the air is of any consequence. Figure 8 shows the oxygen pressures for the various levels at which animals and plants exist on earth.

Most men, of course, live under an oxygen pressure close to that which occurs at sea level—say, from 160 to 120 mm Hg. In the Air Force, when planes fly above 12,000 feet without pressurized cabins, their crews are required to enrich the air they breathe with additional oxygen. The O_2 pressure of the atmosphere at that altitude is about 100 mm Hg. The vital minimum that we can endure is about 65 mm Hg. At this level man begins to lose consciousness as he "ascends" in the low-pressure chamber. It corresponds to an altitude of about 23,000 feet.

During very slow ascents, adaptation to this altitude is possible for several weeks, as various mountain-climbing expeditions in the Himalayas have shown. But permanent settlements are found only up to 15,600 feet in the Andes

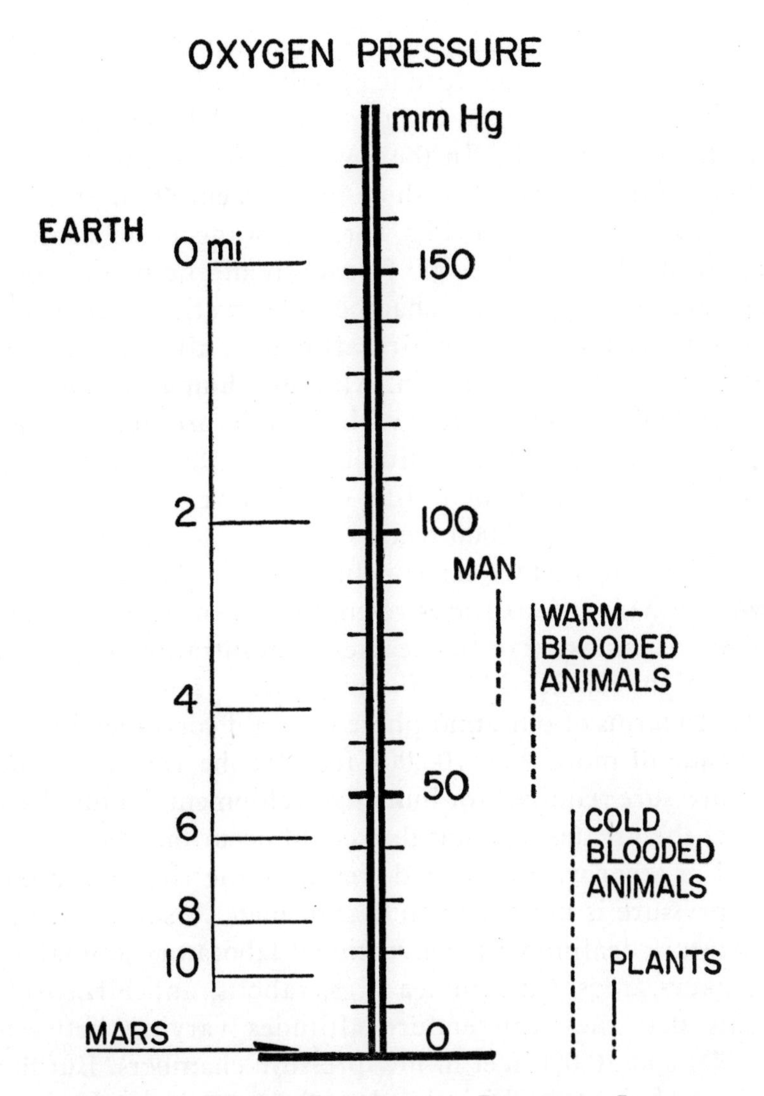

FIGURE 8. OXYGEN PRESSURES AT BIOLOGICAL LEVELS

On the left side of the pressure scale (calibrated in millimeters of mercury) are the corresponding altitudes in miles above the earth and the maximum reading at the surface of Mars. On the right side are the minimum oxygen requirements for men, animals, and plants. It is evident that only the lower types of cold-blooded animals and plants could survive on Mars.

of Chile and Peru. The highest inhabited spot on earth is Jaichan, Tibet, at an altitude of only 15,870 feet.

The oxygen pressure of the air at that height amounts to about 87 mm Hg. In the low-pressure chamber, intellectual faculties begin to show impairment at an O_2 pressure of 100 to 90 mm Hg, corresponding to an altitude between 12,000 and 15,000 feet. It should be pointed out, however, that pressure-chamber observations are taken in fast ascents such as an aircraft makes, allowing no leeway for gradual adaptation. Although human beings can go higher than 15,000 feet with suitable precautions, and even do hard work at altitudes up to 18,000 feet, it is improbable that human life could have originated or developed above 12,000 feet.

From this fact we can conclude certainly that the presence on Mars of creatures resembling men belongs to the realm of fantasy. For the heaviest concentration of oxygen that might conceivably be found on Mars is not over 1 mm Hg. In terms of our atmosphere it would correspond to an altitude of more than 100,000 feet. At the very least, the O_2 pressure required for human development is a hundred times the greatest amount that could occur on Mars.

For other warm-blooded creatures, the vital minimum O_2 pressure is not far from that of men. A survey of the literature dealing with conventional laboratory animals—monkeys, dogs, cats, guinea pigs, rabbits, and birds—reveals that they can endure altitudes varying between 21,000 and 30,000 feet in low-pressure chambers. But the greatest height at which they have been seen to make their homes is not over 16,000 feet, the same peak at which men live.

Eagles and vultures have been observed as high as 27,000 feet over the Himalayas. They were borne up to these lofty altitudes by the powerful updrafts from the giant mountains. Since they were soaring, they used virtually no energy. Their nests and feeding grounds are much farther down.

By and large the minimum oxygen pressure for homoiothermal animals can hardly be less than 60 mm Hg, the pressure found on earth at about 25,000 feet. Even this is many times the best O_2 pressure that could be predicated for Mars. A few rodents (such as mice and hamsters) and bats are somewhat more resistant to oxygen deficiency. The reason is that they are able to lower their body temperature—and thus their need for oxygen—to a considerable degree when oxygen is scarce. In this respect their metabolism shows a link with the cold-blooded animals. Yet they could not survive in an oxygen pressure as low as that of Mars.

The poikilothermal animals, whose body temperature changes with the temperature of their environment, include reptiles, worms, fish, amphibians such as frogs, and other more or less primitive creatures. They can endure oxygen pressures far below 50 mm Hg, down to 5 mm Hg or less. This would correspond on earth to an altitude around 75,000 feet. But they encounter such pressures only under exceptional circumstances. It is hardly probable that they would have developed in the first place under such conditions.

We know that a number of lowly organisms of this type can live for some time without oxygen. They are likely to be found in winter, in ice-covered ponds and lakes under a blanket of snow. There will have been a high consumption of oxygen in such pools, while the absence of light will have hindered production of fresh O_2 by green algae. Examples of this sort may be seen for as long as a month at a time, for instance, in Lake Mendota, Wisconsin. Even though the water is free of oxygen, it still contains abundant life, much of it in a state of rigor due to anoxia.

A special case of anaerobic life is that of worms in the intestines of higher animals, where they find no oxygen. They exist in an atmosphere of methane gas, carbon dioxide, hydrogen, and hydrogen sulphide. But they subsist on foodstuffs already prepared for them that are high in energy. Without this ready-made food supply they would not live.

It would be futile to argue over the existence of such elementary creatures on Mars. They might conceivably be there, granting the extraordinary persistence and adaptability of living matter. It would perhaps create considerable excitement if the first traveler in space should return from Mars to report that he had found a species of microorganism living in the air or on the naked ground. Yet life of this humble order is not what we seek primarily when we study the faces of the neighboring planets. No such microorganism could have developed into a more complex and intelligent sort of life without a rich supply of oxygen, unless it followed some principle totally unknown to us.

So far as animal life is concerned, the possibility of warm-blooded creatures and the higher types of cold-blooded creatures definitely can be eliminated on Mars, because the deficiency of oxygen inhibits them. There remains the fundamentally different problem of the possibility of plant life. There are some clues that point to the presence of a kind of vegetation. These are the green areas which comprise the main topic of this book.

Plant life is the crucial question involved in the possibility of living things on the green and red planet. We shall examine it in detail in the next chapter.

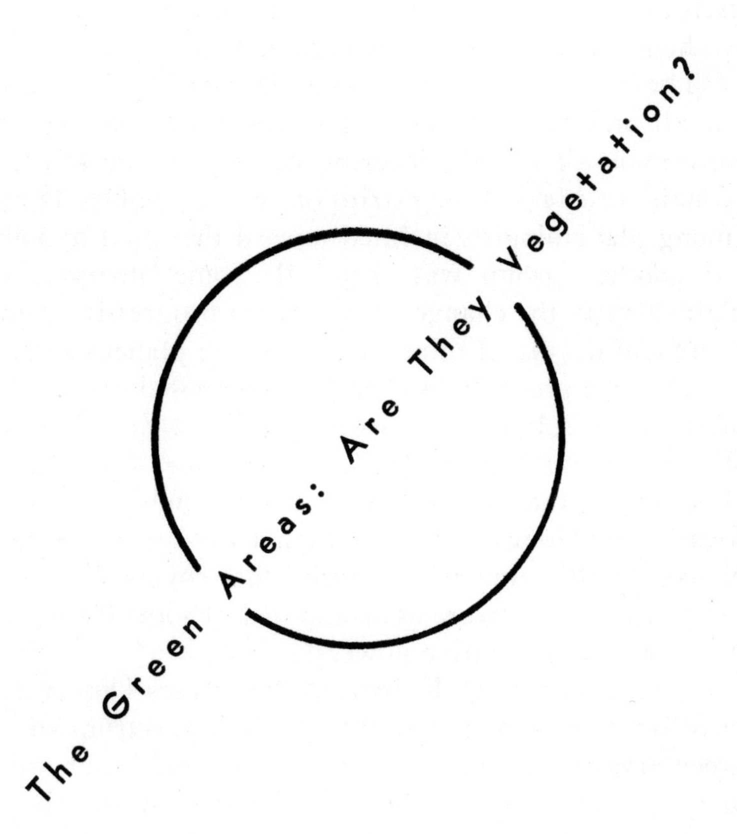

6

Early in the twentieth century, Percival Lowell gave his attention to some fugitive bands of green on Mars that followed the most intriguing course. Over a period of several months the green areas changed to yellow, then to brown, suggesting the seasonal changes in vegetation that occur on the earth. The process repeated itself each year, first in the northern and then in the southern hemisphere, as the polar caps melted.

These areas were later studied in detail by E. M. Antoniadi and E. C. Slipher. Drawings and photographs were made of them. Pickering considered the so-called "canals" of Mars as long strips of vegetation. One faction among planetologists inclined toward the plant hypothesis; another group was skeptical. Some observers explained away the changes in color as a progressive dampening and drying of mineral salts on the planet's surface.

That the green areas cannot be composed of any such inert matter is, however, the opinion of Dr. Ernst J. Opik. Writing recently in the *Irish Astronomical Journal,* Dr. Opik argues that the yellow dust storms which occur on Mars would long since have buried these areas under a blanket of the same arid material that covers the rest of the planet, if they were not composed of some living substance with regenerative powers.

Lately, Gerard P. Kuiper, of the Yerkes Observatory in Wisconsin, found that the infrared spectrum of the green areas is compatible with that of some lower orders of plant life, such as lichens and mosses. With this discovery, the vegetation theory has again become a subject of general interest. What can we say about it from the physiological point of view, especially with regard to the question of oxygen?

It is known that plants breathe and consume oxygen, although they are able to switch to anaerobic respiration at any time. There are some plants that do not stop breathing until the oxygen pressure of the air falls below 1.5 mm Hg—equivalent on earth to an altitude of about 100,000 feet. This pressure is the zero point of plant respiration, and it is almost certainly a good deal higher than any O_2 pressure that may be found on Mars.

When plants are deprived of oxygen and kept in darkness they usually will not grow, and they wither quickly. To grow and develop they need oxygen at a considerably higher pressure than any which the most optimistic astronomer can concede to Mars. Yet, as we saw in Chapter 2, plants have a way to overcome this problem, through a faculty which distinguishes them from all other living things. Provided they have access to sunlight, they can produce their own oxygen by photosynthesis. Their oxygen generators are in their chloroplasts, which contain chlorophyl.

It has been calculated that about 30 square yards of green foliage in daylight produces as much oxygen as a grown man consumes at the same time. The plant cover of a medium-sized state like Missouri yields sufficient oxygen for the whole of mankind. A year's production by the vegetation on all the earth's continents has been computed at 5 billion tons. Truly, this is an extraordinarily important process in the metabolism of nature on earth.

If we assume that vegetation may exist on Mars, what are the chances there for photosynthesis, according to terrestrial concepts? Do the environmental factors on Mars attain the physiological minimum necessary for the process? Or, putting it another way, is the combination of conditions there adequate for this mechanism? We know that photosynthesis needs carbon dioxide and water for its raw materials, as well as sunlight and a certain range of temperature. How do these factors on Mars compare with the physiological requirements for photosynthesis?

The lowest temperature for photosynthesis in most plants is around 32° F, the freezing point of water. Yet in some Arctic lichens it has been found to function in weather close to zero Fahrenheit. During the day on Mars, these temperatures are far exceeded. W. W. Coblentz and C. O. Lampland have observed a rise of temperature to 85° or more above the green areas, as shown in Figure 7.

The amount of sunlight certainly is sufficient for photosynthesis. The solar constant on Mars averages 0.84 gram calories per square centimeter per minute, about 45 per cent of the solar constant on earth. The difference corresponds, as we saw earlier, to the greater distance of Mars from the sun.

We can gain some notion of the intensity of sunlight on Mars if we think of it as the brightness inside a room with the windows open on a cloudless afternoon, or in the shade of an oak forest. Of course the light is direct, not reflected as it would be in such sheltered places, but it is possible that the haze in the Martian atmosphere diffuses it so that it gives much the same effect. Kuiper has suggested that from the surface of Mars the sky might have a pallid, whitish color due to the scattering of light by ice crystals in the upper air. In any case, that is enough light, as we all know, for the growth of many plants on earth that live in shadow.

The exact amount of carbon dioxide necessary for photosynthesis is unknown. But the process has been found at work in the lowest concentrations of CO_2 that have been produced experimentally in laboratories. The most favorable concentration at sea level is from 0.5 to 1 per cent by volume—some fifteen to thirty times the amount that our plants actually have at their disposal in the open air. Carbon dioxide recently has been detected as a definite constituent of the atmosphere of Mars, in proportions greater than on earth. It is reasonable to assume that more than enough CO_2 exists there to support plant life.

Water also now can be taken for granted on Mars. It may occur, however, mainly in the form of snow and vapor. The factor of water is perhaps the weakest one in the planet's combination of conditions for photosynthesis. That is not too strong an argument against vegetation, all the same, if we suppose that the hypothetical plants on Mars may be extremely hygroscopic—that is, able to absorb moisture readily from the air. This is the case on earth with certain fungi and lichens.

The ecological situation on Mars, then, does not unconditionally preclude the possibility of photosynthesis as we know it. Yet it is farther from the optimum than in most regions of the earth. It is perhaps comparable to conditions in the borderlands around the Arctic, or just under the snow-line of very high mountains.

It is therefore improbable that vegetation of an advanced type, such as ferns or seed-bearing plants, will be found on Mars. Their vascular systems demand higher temperatures and greater humidity. Only the lower orders of cellular plants, which are extremely resistant to cold and drought, would be able to endure under such climatic conditions.

Kuiper's spectroscopic observations led him to suggest that plants similar to our lichens and mosses may occur on Mars. Lichens and mosses belong to the two lowest subdivisions of the plant kingdom: the thallophytes, which include algae and lichens, and the bryophytes, which are mosses. The next higher subdivision comprises the pteritophytes, or ferns. After these come the highest (seed-bearing) types, the spermatophytes.

For purposes of planetary ecology, the simpler classification of cellular and vascular plants is sufficient. Only the thallophytes and bryophytes are cellular. All the rest are vascular plants, or tracheophytes. Highly organized varieties such as these are out of the question on Mars, because of its deficiency of heat and moisture.

It might be worth our while now to look more closely at the lichens and mosses. They are the hardiest plants we know. At the top in this respect are lichens, because of their peculiar organization. They consist of two quite dissimilar organisms, a fungus and a number of algae, living together in symbiosis. The fungus component offers protection from cold. Also it provides inorganic substances, including water, thanks to the notably hygroscopic nature of most fungi. The algae components build up organic substances, and supply oxygen through photosynthesis.

Because of this ideal union of their parts, lichens are highly resistant to a dry, cold environment such as they would have on Mars. They make hardly any demands on the ground or other structures that support them. We find them growing on the bark of trees, on the face of rocks, and even on monuments. They inhabit the fossilized trunks of trees in the Petrified Forest of Arizona. In the sub-Arctic regions they are the main type of vegetation, in the form of so-called "reindeer moss." On high mountains they represent the snow-line stage of vegetation. In the Himalayas they are found at altitudes up to 16,000 feet.

In short, these plants are the last outpost of vegetable life. They can exist on rock and calcified remains because they produce organic acids which decompose the stone. By virtue of this talent they are also pioneer plants, preparing the humus for more delicate vegetation. In the course of the earth's history they may well have been the first vegetation, developing on bare volcanic rocks.

Indeed, today they can be seen as the first plants creeping out over the barren lava on extinct volcanoes. At Sunset Crater in Arizona, for example, and on the lava beds near Carrizozo, New Mexico, they give the dark surface of the rock a mottled green appearance.

Liverworts, the most primitive of the mosses, are almost as resistant as lichens. The character of all these plants is adapted particularly to drought and extremes of temperature. With respect to temperature, as we noted earlier, lichens and mosses can endure in a very broad range of heat and cold. They serve as the outstanding example of eurythermia.

It is tempting for the biologist to suppose that plants similar to lichens and mosses may be the last outpost of life on other planets such as Mars, as well as the pioneer vegetation, even if they find no oxygen whatever in the air. It has been suggested that the large quantity of free oxygen in the earth's atmosphere is almost entirely due to the photosynthetic production of plants over the ages. If so, and if O_2 was as scarce at the dawn of life on this planet as it is today on Mars, a start would have had to be made somewhere. Under those conditions, only the lichens and mosses could have made it.

Although, as we have seen, free oxygen is not an absolute necessity for the existence of plants, as carbon dioxide is, they do consume a large amount of oxygen in respiration. And the plants on Mars, if they exist, must have an extremely intense metabolism. The speed with which the green areas expand in the Martian spring would underwrite this assumption. The question then arises: Is a mechanism conceivable that would supply plants not only with carbon dioxide for photosynthesis, but also with oxygen for respiration and with water for both processes?

We do find the prototype of such a system in plants on earth. It is situated in the internal structure of the plants themselves, and does not require oxygen in the atmosphere.

Until now we have dealt only with the physical ecology of Mars, in discussing its hypothetical vegetation. That is to say, we have studied the minimum environmental factors necessary for living processes, and the different types of living matter that are suited to them. In Chapter 2, it was pointed out that a living organism can respond to its environment in such a way as to improve its chances for existence. This is done by adaptation.

In the interest of the supposed vegetation on Mars, then, we are looking for a system in terrestial plants that simultaneously aids the processes of respiration, photosynthesis, and transpiration. If we find it, we are justified in assuming that—by adaptation—it would enable plant life to overcome the oxygen deficiency of Mars.

Such a system is the phenomenon of internal atmosphere, which also was mentioned in Chapter 2. When it is applied to an oxygen-poor and water-poor environment of the kind we see on Mars, it provides a reasonable basis for the assumption that a form of vegetation can survive and maintain itself on that none-too-hospitable planet.

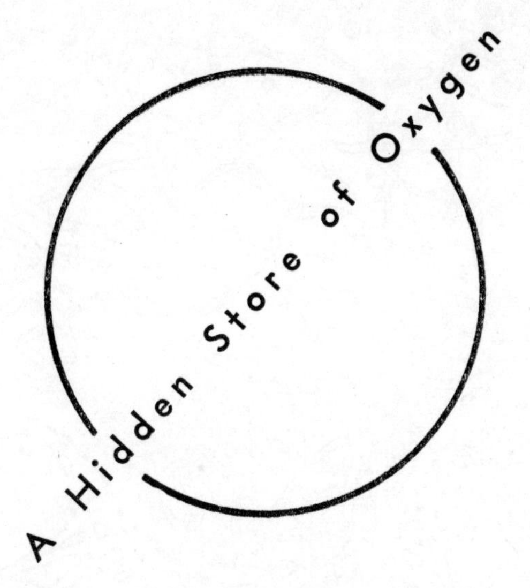

7

For a better understanding of the mechanism which we call the internal atmosphere, suppose for a moment we look at the microscopic structure of plant tissue. Figure 9 shows a cross section through the thallus of a lichen. We notice a dense layer above and below, and

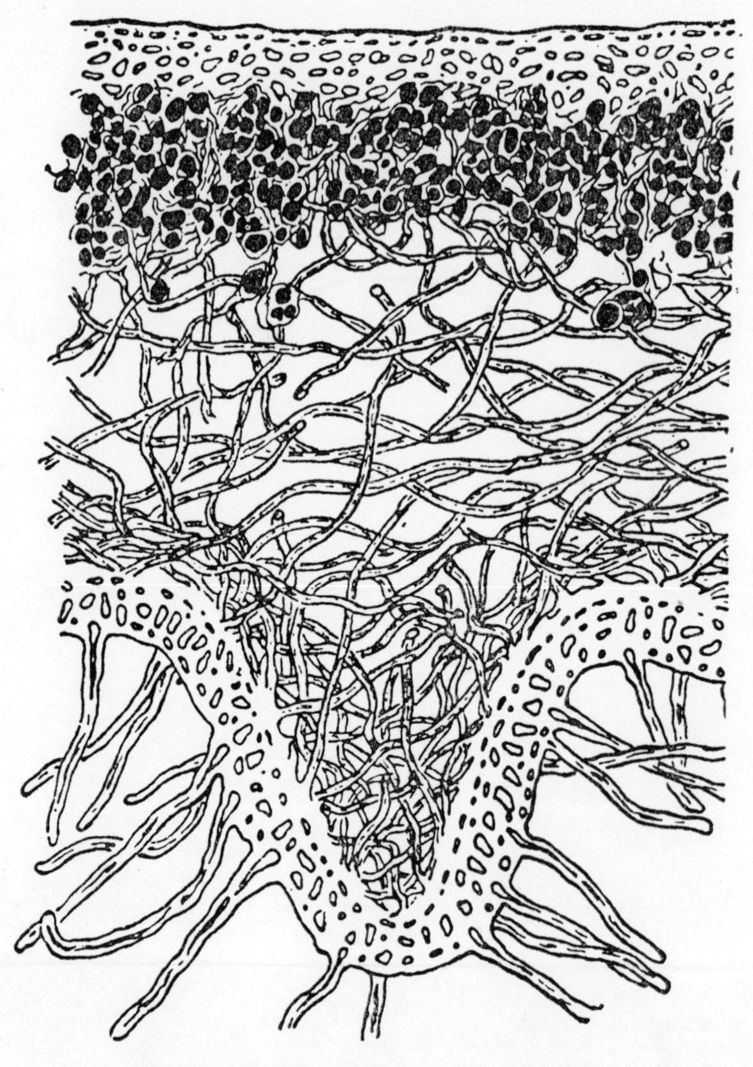

FIGURE 9. CROSS SECTION OF A LICHEN

This section through the thallus of the lichen Lobaria pulmonaria *shows the intercellular air spaces between the dense layers of cells above and below the more attenuated central part of the plant's body.* After Weise from F. Tobler, courtesy J. Springer.

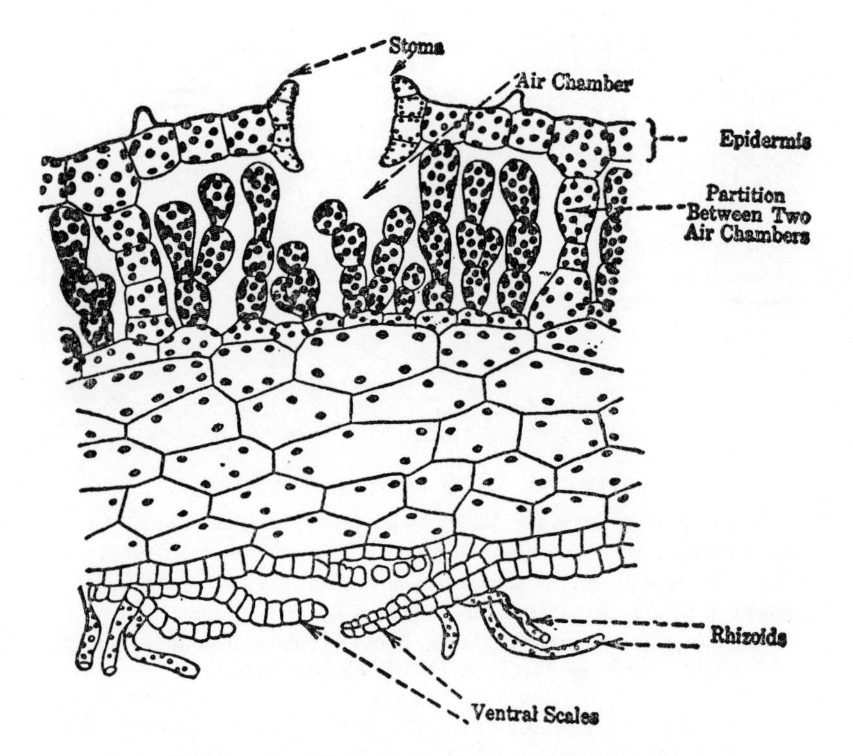

FIGURE 10. CROSS SECTION OF A LIVERWORT

Again the air spaces are seen between the parenchymal cells in the upper part of the thallus of a liverwort. After R. M. Hollman and W. W. Robbins, *General Botany,* courtesy John Wiley and Sons.

a rather tenuous layer in between. Underneath the upper layer a number of algae are imbedded. The layer between exhibits a great many large air spaces.

Figure 10 shows a cross section through the thallus of a liverwort. Again we see the intercellular air spaces, which are walled up into a closed compartment by two columns of cells. The parenchymal cells—supplied with chloroplasts—rise like cactus trees from the base into the air spaces. Besides, we find an opening in the epidermis, called a pore or stoma, leading to the air outside.

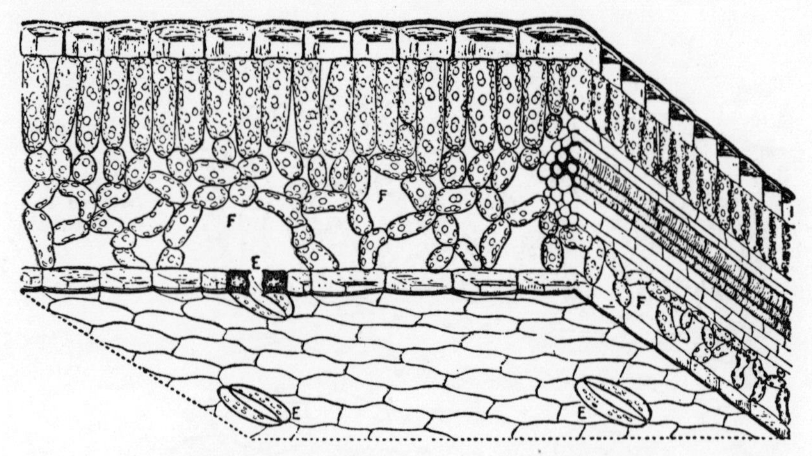

FIGURE 11. CROSS SECTION OF A LEAF

In the leaf of a more highly organized plant, as shown in this sectional view, the intercellular air spaces (F) are very well organized. Access to them from the ambient air outside the epidermis is gained through well-developed stomata—pores—(E), which were seen in the liverwort in a more primitive form. From Sinnoff's *Botany—Principles and Problems,* courtesy McGraw-Hill Book Company.

For us the air spaces and the pores are of special interest. In the higher plants, these air spaces and pores have attained a more advanced stage of development. Figure 11 shows a cut-away view of such a plant. This structure is most pronounced in the leaves of plants that are submerged in water, where it is necessary to provide an adequate inner atmosphere from an outside environment which yields oxygen less readily than air.

This system of intercellular air spaces is known as an aerenchyma. The maze of air passages is so widely spread that virtually every cell of the parenchyma is in contact with internal air. Because of its spongy structure, the inner surface of the leaf is much larger than the outer surface. According to F. M. Turrell (see Bibliography) the ratio of the inner surface to the outer surface in leaves of different species ranges from 10 to 1 to as high as 30 to 1.

The intercellular air spaces are in contact with the outside air through the pores. In lichens, true pores are generally not yet developed. But in many lichens we find cup-like spots of a loose structure, known as cyphellae. The lichen *parmelia exasperata* shows true pores. In the liverworts this mechanism is still further developed, as Figure 10 shows. And the higher plants are equipped with complicated pores which can be adjusted for changing conditions in the air. Several hundred thousand of these pores occupy each square inch on the upper or lower side of the leaf.

The physiological importance of this intercellular air system is obvious. Not only is the area of gas exchange between the leaf and its outside environment enormously increased—reminding us of the inner area of the lungs, which in men may amount to more than 1,000 square feet—but there has also been created a kind of internal atmosphere, more or less independent of the air outside. It is this private atmosphere, not the ambient air, with which the cells are in direct contact.

The inner climate with which the plant supplies itself is more likely to meet the requirements for carbon dioxide, water vapor, and oxygen than is the exterior atmosphere. As we have seen, it serves as a buffer against severe environmental conditions outside. Indeed, this interior breathing system reminds us that neither plants nor animals find even the earth's atmosphere perfectly suited to their needs. They have developed this method of transforming it into an environment that meets their requirements.

So far as the problem of oxygen is concerned, analyses of the intercellular air in plants reveal that it may contain from 30 to 60 per cent oxygen by volume. This means that the O_2 pressure within the leaf can be multiplied temporarily three times above the content of the outer atmosphere, during intensive photosynthesis. Hence, the inner air spaces serve to store surplus oxygen produced by photosynthesis itself.

In this way the system of intercellular air spaces makes the existence of a plant easier in an oxygen-poor or an oxygen-free environment. On earth there is sufficient free oxygen in the air to enable a plant to breathe at night, in the hours of darkness when photosynthesis is suspended. But on a planet such as Mars, which has little or no free oxygen in the air, the plant could produce oxygen by photosynthesis during the day, store the surplus within itself, and use it as needed to provide a reserve energy at times when the photosynthetic product was not available.

Also it should be noted in passing that on such a planet as Mars a plant presumably could produce no oxygen to speak of beyond its own needs, because of the limited supply of water and the reduced amount of energy available from sunlight. Therefore it would not be constantly increasing the hoard of free oxygen in the air, as our plants do. Although there would actually be enough oxygen within the vegetation itself to maintain life, no visible trace of it would be found in the atmosphere. And this is in fact the case on Mars.

The intercellular air spaces offer still another advantage. In freezing weather the formation of ice crystals will occur mainly in these spaces. This is less injurious to the organism than if the ice formation were within the cells themselves.

So the principle of an internal breathing surface and an internal atmosphere is an excellent way for the organism to improve the conditions under which it lives in a severe climate. Suppose the structure of those hypothetical Martian plants had developed along this line. Then the objections that might be advanced against the possibility of vegetation in an oxygen-poor or oxygen-free atmosphere would lose much of their weight. In that case, there would be no reason not to accept—at least tentatively—the logical presumption that the green areas of Mars are precisely what they appear to be: a simple form of vegetable life, growing and receding with the seasons.

If this is so, then it is not beyond the bounds of reasonable speculation to draw the following picture of the organization of plant life on Mars:

Active vegetation there would be possible only on the side of the planet that is exposed at the time to light, as soon after sunrise as the balance of conditions inside the plant became adequate for metabolism. So far as oxygen consumption is concerned, it would depend mainly on the immediate production of O_2 by photosynthesis, plus any small reserve that might be stored in the intercellular air spaces. The greater part of this oxygen would be consumed as it was produced, leaving only a small surplus for the marginal periods of twilight and dawn. In this respect the plants of Mars would differ radically from those on earth, which have at their disposal a surplus in the atmosphere of 1,300 trillion tons (1.3×10^{15}, equivalent to 1.2×10^{21} grams) so that they can breathe also during the night.

On Mars after sunset, oxygen deficiency for plants would soon become acute. But now the arrival of severe cold would be a help, for it puts living matter into a state of dormant life. In this state, since they expend no energy, the plants require no oxygen. In a manner of speaking, they would noctivate, as certain animals and plants on earth hibernate in winter.

Considered in this light, the seeming paradox is revealed that the intense cold of the Martian night actually can be an advantage to the hypothetical vegetation on that planet. For the low temperature after dark could inhibit the damaging effect of the lack of oxygen in the atmosphere. In an oxygen-poor or an oxygen-free environment, the combination of darkness and cold would seem to be preferable for plants to the combination of darkness and warmth. For without sunlight most plants—if they were still active—could survive only as they do on earth, by absorbing enough oxygen to maintain life from the atmosphere around them.

Even on earth, the partial suspension of activity after dark that is manifested in sleep may be connected with the withdrawal of the sun's energy. Though we still have access to vast stores of oxygen in the air, men, animals, and plants perform a ritual resembling noctivation in the hours from dusk to dawn.

Vegetation on Mars must require cold nights because of the hypoxia—or even anoxia—of the air in which they live. Again this is, in fact, the case. It means that plant life on Mars is intermittent, flourishing by day during certain seasons and becoming latent by night. On our own planet, vegetation is, to a lesser extent, intermittent with respect to winter and summer. On Mars, there seems to be no reason why it should not be diurnally as well as annually photorhythmic. Every evening is perhaps a little autumn on that planet, every morning another spring.

In the proterozoic era on earth, a billion years ago, if the temperature and oxygen pressure of the air were lower than they are today—as they may very well have been—life was most probably intermittent in the same way. Only in this manner, perhaps, could life have made a start on earth. For the vast supply of oxygen that we enjoy is an exception, rather than a rule, in the planets which we have been studying. It is more likely one of the products of aboriginal life than a necessary condition for its development.

So, then, it is clear that from a physiological standpoint there are no insurmountable objections to the assumption that some kind of vegetation is seen on Mars. This is all the more true if we give due consideration to the relative nature of the various environmental factors as they are found together—and to the functional adjustments which we know the living organism can make in adapting itself to climatic extremes. Such adjustments are found in great variety among living things on earth. In this light, the oxygen problem offers far less difficulty than is generally supposed. Not oxygen, but carbon dioxide, is the absolute necessity for vegetation. Oxygen it can produce for itself.

As to the apparent absence of oxygen in the Martian atmosphere, we may thus append a physiological footnote to the astrophysical text. Although there may indeed be no atmospheric oxygen on Mars, it is still quite possible that there is an invisible layer of oxygen concealed within the vegetation on that planet. Maintained at the proper temperature and humidity, it would constitute a sort of "underground atmosphere," circling once daily like a tide around the globe in company with the sun.

This biospheric atmosphere, if it exists, would naturally escape the eye of an astronomer. For it would be consumed so rapidly, during the plant's day-long period of activity, that no appreciable part of it would ever remain to build an oxygen reservoir in the atmosphere. It would be, in fact, an inner air that we could only detect by observations made on the planet itself. As Vaucouleurs suggests, some of the underground oxygen may be locked up in the ferrous oxide of limonite ($2Fe_2O_33H_2O$) which he believes to be the constituent of the soil of Mars that is responsible for its ruddy appearance.

In these last chapters, we have discussed only the possibility on Mars of men, animals, and green plants. The first two we have ruled out because they need large quantities of free oxygen which they cannot find on Mars. Green plants we may consider possible, because they are able to produce oxygen for themselves. There still remains one other class of living things: the chemoautotrophs, a type of primitive animal life which, like plants, produces its own organic substance.

As we remarked in Chapter 2, the chemoautotrophs require no sunlight. Instead, they draw their energy from inorganic matter like hydrogen, methane, ammonia, and so on, by oxidation. But for this process they do require oxygen. It is just possible that the low content of oxygen in the Martian atmosphere may be enough for these elemental creatures, which are all bacteria of various kinds. They could, perhaps, even live directly on the oxygen produced by vegetation. This would be another factor preventing the escape of oxygen into the atmosphere.

The atmosphere of Mars, like that of the earth, has very little of such gases as methane and hydrogen. The chemoautotrophs would be of more interest in a discussion of possible life in the so-called protoatmospheres, which are asumed to have blanketed the planets in their formative stage. They probably were rich in methane, hydrogen, and ammonia. These gases also are found—along with water—in the present atmospheres of the larger planets like Jupiter and Saturn.

The bacteria of which we speak could have existed in the protoatmospheres, if other factors such as temperature were favorable. It is even possible that they were the very first kind of living thing on earth and the other planets. But this is a speculation that leads us far afield from the green areas on the Red Planet, into the realm of general planetary ecology.

Mars, like the earth, is not a protoplanet but a terrestrial globe some three billion years old. Most of its hydrogen, methane, and ammonia are long since gone. If it has such bacteria today, they cannot be of any great importance in that planet's biological outlook. And they can hardly have evolved beyond the primitive stage in which we find them on earth. At most they, might someday, prove to be a biological curiosity for scientists exploring the surface of Mars.

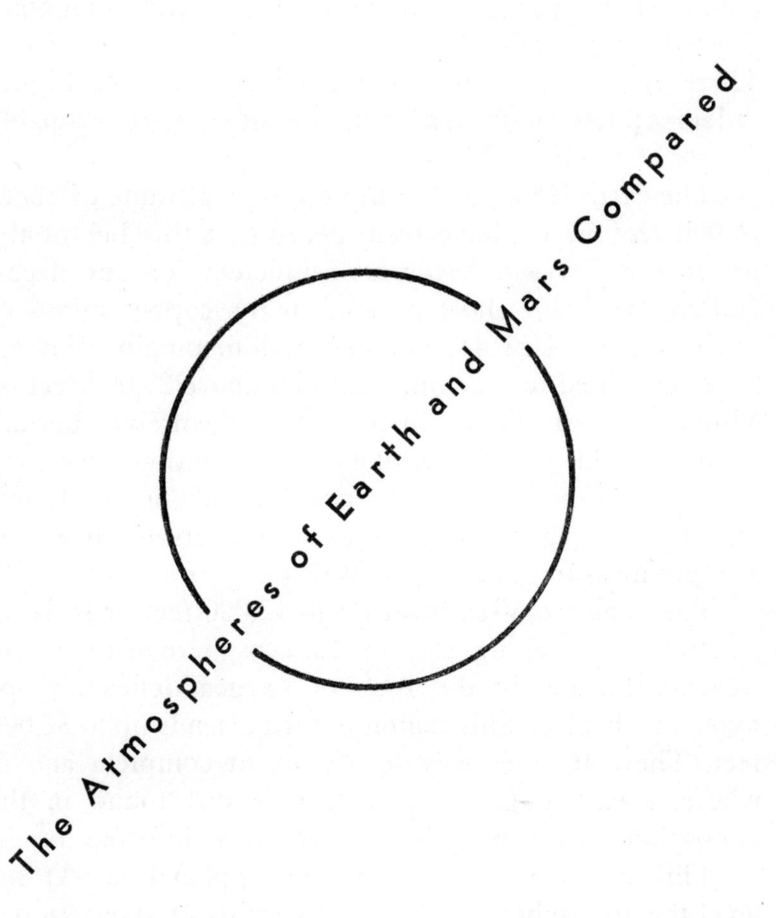

8

In earlier chapters we dealt with the physiological qualities of the atmosphere of Mars. They will become still more clear if we examine them by comparison with our own atmosphere, using some recent concepts of its physiological functions. The material for such a study has been supplied in recent years by high-mountain physiology, by aviation medicine, and by space medicine. These researches reinforce the conclusion that higher orders of life, with reasoning faculties, very probably cannot be found on Mars.

The earth is inhabited only up to an altitude of about 16,000 feet, as we have seen, because at this height the pressure of oxygen becomes insufficient for our needs. Indians work for short periods in the copper mines of Peru at a level of 18,000 feet, and mountain climbers have succeeded in reaching altitudes above 29,000 feet on Mount Everest. They did not adapt themselves permanently to such a dizzy eminence. Adaptation over long periods of time seems to be possible only up to 16,000 feet. Extra oxygen is considered a necessity for flyers, as a safety measure, above 12,000 feet.

The zone from sea level up to 12,000 feet or so is, in a manner of speaking, the vertical ecosphere of the earth. Beyond this height the zone of oxygen deficiency—or hypoxia—begins. This region in turn extends up to 52,000 feet. There it gives way to a zone of complete anoxia where, even though some oxygen is still found in the atmosphere, we can no longer receive it into our lungs.

This peculiar fact requires an explanation. At sea level the atmosphere of the earth consists of about 78 per cent nitrogen by volume, 21 per cent oxygen, and 0.03 per cent carbon dioxide. The remaining 1 per cent is mainly argon, with neon, helium, and hydrogen in minute traces. Water vapor varies between zero and 4 per cent, reducing the others proportionately when it is at its peak; and the amount of it in the air depends on the temperature. All the values given in this discussion are in round numbers, as far as possible.

In millimeters of mercury, the pressures of the principal gases in the atmosphere at sea level amount to roughly 595 mm Hg of nitrogen, 160 mm Hg of oxygen, and 0.23 mm Hg of carbon dioxide. Water vapor may come to as much as 30 mm Hg. The total atmospheric pressure is 760 mm Hg.

Now, in breathing, this air is drawn into the small lung spaces—known as alveoli—and is mixed with more carbon dioxide and water vapor, both of them produced in the body. Thus a different gaseous mixture is formed. In the lungs it contains about 75 per cent nitrogen and argon by volume, 14 per cent oxygen, 6 per cent water vapor, and 5 per cent carbon dioxide.

These values in millimeters of mercury correspond to 570 mm Hg of nitrogen, 105 mm Hg of oxygen, 47 mm Hg of water vapor, and nearly 40 mm Hg of carbon dioxide. In the lungs, too, the total pressure is 760 mm Hg.

Both nitrogen and oxygen enter the alveolar spaces from outside, while carbon dioxide and water vapor are produced mostly in the body. Thus the first two constituents depend on the air around us, the other two on the body itself, including its temperature.

Hence, with increasing altitude, the amount of nitrogen and oxygen in the lungs decreases, as it does in the ambient air outside. But water vapor and CO_2 remain fairly constant, since they are formed in the body. Together they maintain a pressure of about 87 mm Hg.

If we rise to an altitude where the atmospheric pressure drops to this value, no outside air—and consequently no oxygen—can enter the lungs. The reason is that they already are occupied by carbon dioxide and water vapor to the full pressure of the air. This would be true even if the outside atmosphere consisted of pure oxygen.

Thus we are faced at such an altitude with an environment from which it is no longer possible to receive any oxygen—in spite of the fact that oxygen is there—for purely physiological reasons. This situation arises at 52,000 feet. Here, then, the total anoxia zone of our atmosphere begins, regardless of the fact that oxygen is found in the same proportion as at sea level. In other words, the ability of the atmosphere to supply us with life-giving oxygen has dropped to zero.

If the crew members of a plane should be suddenly exposed to the outside air at this altitude by a leak in the pressurized cabin, they would find themselves totally without a fresh supply of oxygen. Unless additional protection were afforded by pressure suits, they would have to fall back on the small oxygen reserves in their blood and tissues. These would last for about fifteen seconds. After that, they would lose consciousness and the power to save themselves.

This knowledge has been gained largely from experiments in explosive decompression—the laboratory equivalent of puncturing a pressurized cabin—in low-pressure chambers especially designed for aeromedical research. From these experiments we conclude that, if the physiological zero point for the intake of oxygen is reached at 52,000 feet, the amount of oxygen in the air as we go still higher is no longer of any consequence, even in the depths of interplanetary space.

At 52,000 feet we have reached infinity, so far as oxygen is concerned. To the extent that oxygen is an essential part of our environment, we have arrived in space; for in this respect the situation a mere ten miles up is no better than it will be no matter how many thousands of miles we travel toward the stars thereafter.

Thus we see that there are "space-equivalent" regions within our own atmosphere. The space-equivalent altitude for oxygen is the first of these, and one of the most important. Others are found as we proceed higher. At about 63,000 feet a second border of space is passed, where the air pressure drops below 47 mm Hg. This is the vapor pressure of body liquids, including blood and tissue fluids, at 98.6° F, the normal temperature of the body. If the air pressure drops to this value or below, the body fluids will begin to boil. For the air pressure is then too low to keep water in a liquid state at body temperature.

Putting it differently, the heat required to boil water has dropped at this altitude—because of the lowered pressure—from 212° F, as it is at sea level, to 98.6°, the temperature of the human body. That this is the case has been shown in laboratory tests by Major General Harry G. Armstrong.

Still higher up, space-equivalent conditions of physiological importance are met as the filtering function of the atmosphere decreases. These have to do with solar and cosmic radiation, and with meteors.

The ultraviolet band of solar radiation is of the greatest biological significance. It is that part of the electromagnetic spectrum which produces erythema—sunburn—on the human skin if it is exposed to intense sunlight. Normally we are protected against this radiation, because ultraviolet rays are largely absorbed by the ozone in the atmosphere. This particular form of oxygen—with three atoms instead of two or one—is distributed thinly in the atmosphere between 50,000 and 140,000 feet, with its greatest density at about 80,000 feet.

Above the ozonosphere protection against ultraviolet radiation ceases. At that height—about fifteen miles—we find ourselves on another border of space within our atmosphere.

As with ultraviolet radiation, so with cosmic rays. Coming from somewhere out in space, and loaded with tremendous energy, they continuously bombard our atmosphere. The primary rays, consisting 99 per cent of protons and the rest of heavy atomic nuclei, are absorbed in the layers from 80,000 to 120,000 feet above the earth, and transformed into secondary rays of less toxic quality by interaction with the molecules of the air. But higher than 120,000 feet—or twenty-two miles—we meet the cosmic rays in their primary form. How much damage they may do to human tissues is still a matter of discussion.

Of cosmic origin, too, are most meteors. These are usually absorbed in the atmosphere from 400,000 feet to 260,000 feet above the ground. Beyond this region they are found as in free space—except that half of them are shielded from the flyer by the earth's own bulk. The same thing is true, incidentally, of cosmic rays.

These successive borderlines, at which the functions of the atmosphere one by one lose their physiological effectiveness, create a sort of twilight zone between our atmosphere and space. The term "aeropause" has been coined to designate this region, which is not a functioning atmosphere in the ecological sense, and yet is not absolute space because atmospheric gases are still present in it. We might say that it represents—from our point of view—a kind of pseudospace. From the point of view of one watching us from the cosmos, it is a kind of pseudoatmosphere.

This zone begins, as we have seen, at an altitude of about 52,000 feet, where the air pressure is about 87 mm Hg. Now, the atmosphere of Mars on its surface has an air pressure of about 65 to 70 mm Hg, according to the most recent estimates. Hence the air pressure on the surface of Mars is about equal to that found at an altitude of 56,000 feet on earth. It is already in the equivalent of our aeropause, above the level where we are able to receive oxygen from the air.

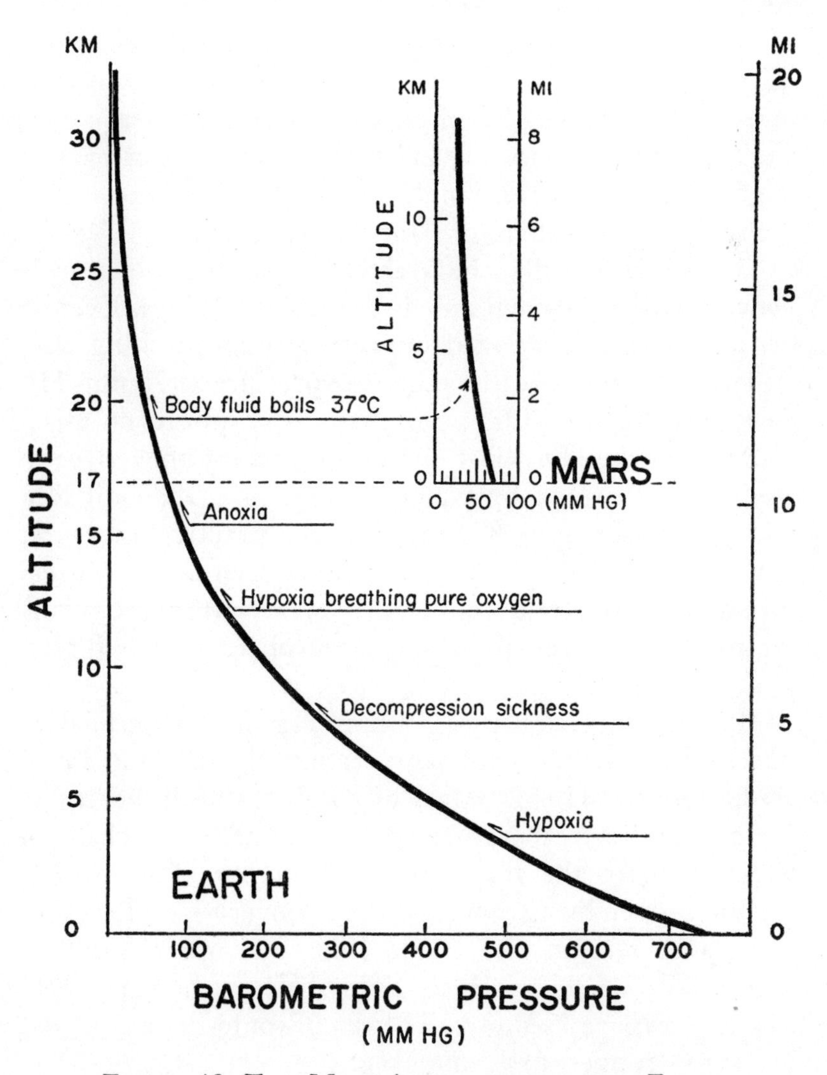

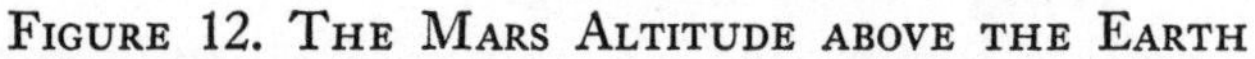
FIGURE 12. THE MARS ALTITUDE ABOVE THE EARTH

The altitudes and pressures of the Martian atmosphere are here projected onto those of the earth. The curve shows points at which certain physiological effects of decreasing pressure are observed.

In Figure 12 the air pressure of Mars with relationship to that of the earth at an equivalent altitude is pictured. In addition, the physiological borderlines which we have just discussed are indicated. In the upper part of the figure, at the corresponding pressure altitude on earth, the surface atmosphere of Mars is shown.

Thus it is seen that the Martian atmosphere starts well above the point of total anoxia for human beings. Even if the air of Mars contained pure oxygen and nothing else, we still could not breathe it. At the pressure of 70 mm Hg on the surface of Mars no oxygen—and indeed no air—could enter the alveoli of our lungs, because they already would be occupied by water vapor and carbon dioxide with a pressure up to 87 mm Hg. As a practical measure, a man on Mars would have to take oxygen under a pressure about three times that of the surface air, corresponding to the total pressure of our atmosphere at 30,000 feet, in order to survive.

In the air pressure of 70 mm Hg on the surface of Mars, water will boil at a temperature of 110° F, as Lowell first noted. This is a fact of considerable importance, for a climatic temperature of 110° is never reached on Mars, even in the tropics in midsummer. The highest readings given by astronomers are not over 87°. Therefore water will remain in a liquid state, and not dissolve in vapor. Nor would our body fluids boil on the surface of Mars, as Figure 13 shows. This they would do only if the pressure dropped to 47 mm Hg.

On earth this pressure is found at an altitude of 63,000 feet, only 7,000 feet beyond the level corresponding to the surface of Mars. On Mars the same pressure is met nearly 13,000 feet above the ground. In that atmosphere it is possible to rise almost twice as far as in ours with the same decrease in pressure. The reason for this is that the density

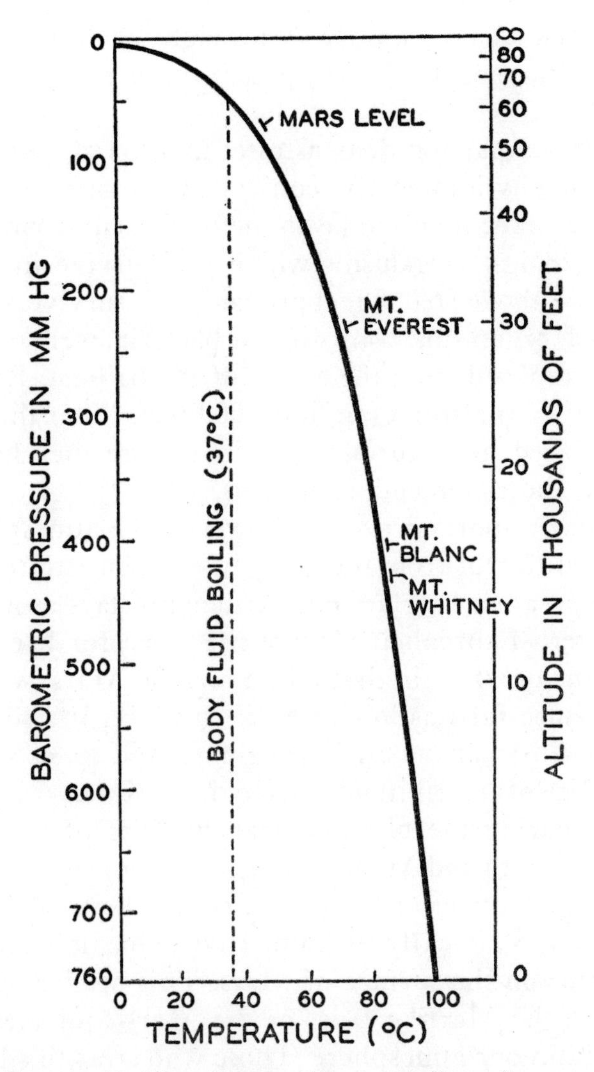

FIGURE 13. THE BOILING POINT OF BODY LIQUIDS

It varies, as this chart shows, according to the barometric pressure at different altitudes. The crucial height at which it drops to body temperature (37° C or 98.6° F), and the body fluids begin to boil, is not reached until well above the pressure on the surface of Mars.

of air falls off less rapidly with height on Mars, because the gravitational field has a much smaller gradient than our own.

This comparison demonstrates that the atmosphere of Mars is physiologically equivalent to our aeropause, which we have found to be an ineffective environment for human beings. Organisms which can survive in our atmosphere above 56,000 feet probably can survive on Mars too. Such organisms, consisting of bacteria, were collected in air samples during the ascent of the balloon, Explorer II, in 1935, at altitudes up to 65,000 feet. Later these bacteria, placed in cultures, grew. Therefore they had survived at those tremendous heights.

In one important respect, however, the atmosphere of Mars is different from the aeropause. In our stratosphere, the temperature is relatively constant: it stays around 65° below zero Fahrenheit. Active life, even for bacteria, is out of the question in that frigid air. On Mars, while the temperature falls as low as −95° at night, it also ranges as high as 85° above during the day. And so, as we have seen, a life of intermittent activity is possible.

Comparing the physiological qualities of the atmospheres of earth and Mars also demonstrates another point. This is, that a flyer or balloonist, rising above 56,000 feet, is exposed to virtually the same environmental conditions that occur on the surface of Mars. This borderline is, so to speak, the Martian level or the Mars-equivalent altitude within our atmosphere. Those who cross this line are entering, as it were, the atmosphere of Mars while they are still a mere ten and one-half miles above our own planet. If they are able to survive in our aeropause with proper training and equipment, they will be able to survive on Mars.

And that, too, opens an intriguing possibility. It is highly improbable that we will find any beings like ourselves living in the thin air on that planet. Yet with a few mechanical aids—of a sort that we now supply to pilots soaring into the upper levels of the atmosphere—a man should be able to maintain himself on Mars for a considerable time without discomfort. Once granting that he could get there, an explorer should find the environment on Mars no more difficult than, say, the Antarctic.

One age-old ally he would not have, to comfort him in the icy Martian night. That ally is fire, which the poet Schiller saluted as "the free daughter of nature." Here on earth we take its power for granted, as an agent both of progress and of destruction. It was fire that first gave us metal to replace our clumsy tools of wood and flint. Fire burns the fuel in our automobile and aircraft engines. Without it, we would have nothing remotely resembling our civilization.

On Mars there is no fire. There can be none. For fire is a kind of combustion, like life itself, that requires free oxygen in the air for its consumption. All fire extinguishers depend for their effect on various methods of blocking the access of oxygen to the blaze. And as oxygen is progressively withdrawn at increasing altitudes, fire suffers from hypoxia just as living creatures do.

This gradual sickening may be seen by watching the flame of a candle in a low-pressure chamber. In the series of five photographs in Plate IV, a candle is shown first at sea level, then at 16,000, at 32,000, at 48,000, and finally at 65,000 feet. It grows steadily more feeble until, at eighteen miles, the slightest breath of wind will blow it out. We may consider 65,000 feet the limit beyond which a flame will not burn.

At this level in our sky the oxygen pressure is around 10 mm Hg. But on Mars even that much oxygen is never found. The greatest O_2 pressure available there is probably less than 1 mm Hg, corresponding to the concentration in our air above 100,000 feet. This is another respect in which the atmosphere of Mars differs from our stratosphere.

And so we can assume that fire will not burn on Mars. An automobile or a conventional airplane would be as useless there as a box of matches, without special oxygen equipment for the engine. So would a cigarette lighter or a gas stove or a good five-cent cigar. Cooking would be impossible by any means except electricity. And in late summer on Mars, no racing prairie fires will ever sweep across the parched vegetation, destroying the plants that have struggled so hard for life in that arid land.

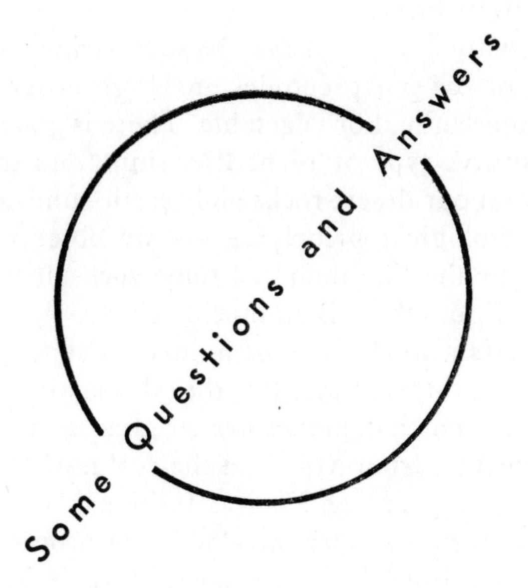

9

The deductions we have made in this book are not, perhaps, wholly satisfying to a gregarious mind that hopes to find companionship wherever it may roam in space. Nor is there anything really startling about the picture we have drawn of life on Mars, as it may exist in the light of biological laws on earth. Other writers—notably Gerard P. Kuiper—have touched in passing on the same possibility. Our function has been mainly to confirm it from the outlook of a physiologist, and to show the mechanism by which a rather limited kind of life could maintain itself there.

The situation on Mars may be summarized as follows. The lack of oxygen precludes any high order of living things, either animal or vegetable. There is good evidence for a primitive type of plant life, similar to the lichens that grow on our desert rocks and Arctic tundras, and we find that biological principles—as we observe them on earth—favor the likelihood of some such elemental species. In addition, there is an outside chance that we might find on Mars a lowly type of animal existence: bacteria of some kind, for example. But the odds against any intelligent beings on that planet are so great as to place the idea of "visitors from Mars" in the realm of fantasy.

Until some years ago, it was fashionable to interpret Mars as an aging sphere on which the processes of life had once flourished but were now dying, if indeed they had not vanished. The earth, according to this view, was still in the springtime of its youth; while Venus was an adolescent world, covered perhaps by the primordial sea, at the dawn of life where the earth had stood geological ages ago.

The foundation for this extremely dismal notion was the old nebular hypothesis, used to explain the creation of the solar system. It was supposed that an incandescent cloud of gas, as it condensed to form the sun, threw off large, blazing hot globules. They gradually cooled, solidified, and became the planets. By this model of creation, the planets were formed at different times. Primarily on the basis of visual observation, astronomers assigned them their ages and made these arbitrary assumptions about their stages of development.

The nebular theory long since has been discarded by most astrophysicists. It was superseded first by the planetesimal hypothesis of Thomas C. Chamberlin and Forest R. Moulton half a century ago, modifying the beliefs of its originator, the 19th Century French astronomer, Laplace. Out of their theory has come in recent years a new concept of the origin of our universe, propounded by Carl von Weizsäcker, D. ter Haar, Harold C. Urey, and others. According to this theory, the sun and planets all collected simultaneously from a diffuse cloud of gas, dust, and larger particles in space. Originally very cold, they passed through various temperature phases, ranging from far below freezing to 4,000° F and much higher in the case of the sun.

If that is so, the planets and the sun are all of the same age. Whether they exhibit the characteristics of a dead world or of a living one would depend on local conditions in the region of their formation, and on their distance from the heat of the sun.

Now, it entertains a physiologist to imagine that, if any of our planets are biologically "older" than the others, they would be the ones nearer to the sun. As in the tropics on earth, compared with the colder areas of Northern Europe, their entire metabolism might have been speeded up by the increased intensity of heat radiation. Life would have appeared sooner—if at all—and run its course long before the outer planets were ready to produce it by their sluggish processes. Not Mars but Venus would be the "aging" planet on the verge of life's extinction. And Mars would be the adolescent, standing where the earth once stood at the dawn of living matter.

The idea is a novel one, and I do not put it forward as a biological theory, though it finds some confirmation in J. Wasiutynski's hydrodynamic system of planetary development. In any case, it has this virtue: it serves to remind us that Mars, because it shows no sign of present life on a high level, is not necessarily a "dead" or "dying" planet. The same argument can be advanced as easily to show that Mars is at the beginning of its biological development. Or it may well be that Mars, throughout all its geological ages, never has and never will support a form of life above the most primitive kind. We only know with some assurance that it does not seem to just now.

Even this opinion is at the moment entirely theoretical. It is based on facts known to us about Mars as an environment, revealed in the last fifty years or so by astronomers and physicists, and on facts known to us about the behavior of life in our own environment, compiled over centuries of observation by physiologists and—in recent decades—by students of aviation medicine. The two sets of facts, balanced one against the other, strongly suggest a situation of the sort we have described. But they do not confirm it.

There is great need for a research laboratory, here on earth, in which conditions as they are found on other planets could be reproduced as a setting for biological experiments. The versatility of life is so boundless, its determination to survive and flourish so acute, that no one can say with absolute certainty that it might not find ways to adapt itself in almost any set of circumstances it would meet on terrestrial bodies elsewhere in the universe. Only by laboratory demonstration can we reach a positive answer to these questions.

Fortunately, there exists the prototype of such a laboratory. In the low-pressure chambers and the climatic chambers that aviation medicine has built and operated during the last twenty years, we can produce artificially almost any degree of atmospheric pressure or temperature encountered in planetary environments in our solar system. Some of the most vital information used in this book has come from experiments in high-altitude physiology, with chambers of this kind, at the Air Force School of Aviation Medicine and at other aeromedical research centers.

It would take only minor modifications and adjustments to construct a "Mars chamber" capable of reproducing very nearly the exact environmental conditions—in so far as we know them—on that planet, or indeed on any planet from Mercury to Pluto. By adding or subtracting atmospheric gases in the proper proportions, under various intensities of heat or cold, we could determine with a fair degree of accuracy what the reactions of different organisms would be to those climatic variations. Only one important factor could not be created synthetically in such a chamber—the force of gravity. Until now, we have no means of altering this planetary characteristic in the laboratory.

Which is to say that even the Mars chamber—far as it would go toward solving the problems of planetary ecology—is not the ultimate answer. The only way we shall ever know conclusively what life, if any, is on Mars will be to travel there and see it—so to speak—in the flesh. The Mars chamber is only an instrument with which to make preliminary studies, in order to overcome all the obstacles we can in advance.

A great many distinguished scientists, including aircraft engineers and rocket experts as well as astrophysicists, believe that the day is not too far off when we shall undertake the exploration of space in all seriousness. The technical facilities to launch a manned rocket into the solitude beyond the earth's atmosphere already are available to us. We await only the money and the concerted effort required for such a prodigious undertaking.

When that day comes, no one will be more agreeably surprised than myself to find—or, better, to hear—that the conclusions reached in this book are utterly wrong. The limited facts with which we have to deal at this time point in no other direction. Yet I would be pleased to learn that some crucial factor is omitted in these calculations, and that life exists in an advanced state of organization on Mars.

I suppose, as children, all of us have wrestled with the question whether it was more reasonable to imagine the cosmos as being finite or infinite, transient or eternal, until Einstein determined for us that it is both. The physiologist wrestles with a similar enigma. On the one hand, his knowledge tells him that no neighboring planet in our solar system offers the unique combination of circumstances favorable to life that we enjoy on earth. On the other, reason says it is most unlikely that a chemical reaction so various and complex should occur on only one of a dozen or more terrestrial orbs in our part of the universe.

The tantalizing glimpses which we get of these neighboring bodies in our telescopes are by no means encouraging. Some, like Venus, are hidden under a blanket of atmosphere so impenetrable that we can detect no sign of activity whatever beneath it. Others, like our closest companion, the Moon, are quite evidently barren and untenanted. Yet, if the same physical principles that gave us our abode are at work everywhere in the cosmos, as they seem to be, we hesitate to believe that the highest expression of those principles in our experience—rational life—is found only here, as it were by accident.

The human mind leans intuitively toward the conviction that there are beings of our own kind elsewhere in space, if not in this particular area of it, then in some other. Catholic theologians have long declared that the possibility of inhabited worlds besides our own is in accord with the doctrine of the Church.* It would be rash of any writer to assert categorically, from the inconclusive evidence we now have, that life of an order comparable to ours is impossible on Mars or on any other planet known to us. We can only say—regretfully—that it seems unlikely, in view of the physiological limitations that apply to life on earth.

And there we leave the question, until that day when the first traveler steps out of a space ship onto the green and red planet. It will be for him to tell us whether he finds an exotic vista of living things, burgeoning luxuriantly by processes unknown to us; or a simple prospect of humble lichens, reviving and declining with the seasons, as this book suggests; or a lifeless landscape stretching monotonously to the horizon, on which some optical illusion like a mirage produces the effect that appears to us as vegetation.

Let us hope at least that what he sees is not the last and most melancholy of these spectacles.

* See, for example, this statement by the Dutch seholar, Father George Van Noort, in his *Treatise on God the Creator,* published in 1920: "A person would not violate the faith who would believe that there are certain rational creatures on other heavenly bodies." See also a discussion of this point by Father Francis J. Connell, C.Ss.R., in *The Monitor,* San Francisco, Calif., August 8, 1952.

BIBLIOGRAPHY

I: Astronomy and Astrophysics

Books

Antoniadi, E. M., *La Planète Mars*. Paris: 1930.

Arrhenius, S. A., *Werden der Welten*. Leipzig: Akad. Verlagsgesellschaft, 1908.

Braun, W. von, *Das Marsprojekt*. Frankfurt: Umschauverlag, 1952.

Clarke, A. C., *The Exploration of Space*. New York: Harper and Bros., 1951.

Flammarion, C., *La Pluralité des Mondes Habitées*. Paris: 1862.

Gamow, G., *The Biography of the Earth*. New York: Viking Press, 1941.

Jones, H. S., *Life on Other Worlds*. New York: The Macmillan Co., 1940.

Kuiper, G. P., *The Atmospheres of the Earth and Planets*. Chicago: University of Chicago Press, 1951.

Ley, W., *The Conquest of Space*. New York: Viking Press, 1949.

———, *Rockets, Missiles, and Space Travel*. New York: Viking Press, 1951.

Lowell, P., *Mars and Its Canals*. New York: The Macmillan Co., 1906.

———, *Mars as the Abode of Life*. New York: The Macmillan Co., 1908.

———, *The Evolution of Worlds*. New York: The Macmillan Co., 1909.

Maunder, E. W., *Are the Planets Inhabited?* New York: Harper and Bros., 1913.

Pickering, W. H., *Mars*. Boston: R. G. Badger, 1921.

Rankama, K., and T. G. Sahama, *Geochemistry*. Chicago: University of Chicago Press, 1950.

Urey, H. C., *The Planets, Their Origin and Development*. New Haven: Yale University Press, 1952.

Vaucouleurs, G. de, *The Planet Mars*. Translated by T. A. Moore. London: Faber and Faber, 1950.

———, *Physique de la Planète Mars*. Paris: Albin Michel, 1951.

Whipple, F. L., *Earth, Moon, and Planets*. Philadelphia: The Blakiston Co., 1946.

Articles and Papers

Adams, W. S., and T. Dunham, Jr., Ap. J., 39:308 (1934).

Coblentz, W. W., and C. O. Lampland, *Further Radiometric Measurements and Temperature Estimates of the Planet Mars*. Washington: U. S. Government Printing Office, 1927.

Herzberg, G., *The Atmospheres of the Planets*. J. Royal Astron. Soc. of Canada, 45:100(1951).

Hess, S. H., *Some Aspects of the Meteorology of Mars*. J. Meteorol., 7:1 (1950).

LaPaz, L., *Meteoroids, Meteorites, and Hyperbolic Meteoritic Velocities.* Chapter XIX, *Physics and Medicine of the Upper Atmosphere.* Albuquerque, University of New Mexico Press, 1952.

———, *The Nortonite Fall and its Mineralogy.* Am. Mineralogist, 36:45 (1951).

Öpik, E. J., Irish Astr. J., I:45 (1950).

Slipher, E. C., *The Planets.* Proc. Am. Philosoph. Soc., 79, No. 3 (1938).

Vaucouleurs, G. de, *Physics of the Planet Mars.* Astron. Soc. Pacific, No. 276 (1952).

Wasiutynski, J., *Hydrodynamics and Structure of Stars and Planets.* Oslo: Astrophysica Norvegica, Vol. 4 (1946).

Wright, W. H., *Photographs of Mars Made with Light of Different Colors.* Publ. Astron. Soc. Pacific, 36:239 (1924).

II: Biology, Medicine, and Aviation Medicine

Books

Allee, W. C., A. E. Emerson, O. Park, T. Park, and K. T. Schmidt, *Principles of Animal Ecology.* Philadelphia: W. B. Saunders, 1949.

Armstrong, H. G., *Principles and Practice of Aviation Medicine.* Baltimore: Williams and Wilkins, 1952.

Bauer, L. H., *Aviation Medicine.* Williams and Wilkins, 1926.

Belchradek, J., *Temperatur und lebende Materie.* Berlin: Bornträger, 1935.

Buddenbrook, W. von, *Grundriss der Vergl. Physiologie.* Berlin: Bornträger, 1937.

Dill, D. B., *Life, Heat, and Altitude.* Cambridge: Harvard University Press, 1938.

Grandpierre, R., *Eléments de Médecine Aéronautique.* Paris: 1948.

Harrow, B., *Biochemistry.* Philadelphia: W. B. Saunders, 1946.

Heilbrunn, L. V., *General Physiology.* Philadelphia: W. B. Saunders, 1949.

Kanitz, A., *Temperatur und Lebensvorgänge in Allgemeinen.* In *Tabulae Biologicae,* Edited by W. Jung. Berlin: 1926.

Kostychew, S., *Pflanzenatmung.* Berlin: J. Springer, 1944.

Liebig, J. von, *Organische Cheme in ihrer Anwending auf Agrikultur und Physiologie.* Braunschweig: 1849.

Lo Monaco, G. T., *Elementi di Fisiologia Patologia dell' uomo in volo.* Rome: Abruzzino Editore, 1948.
Luyet, B. J., and P. M. Gehenio, *Life and Death at Low Temperatures.* Normandy, Missouri: Biodynamica, 1949.
Marbarger, J. P., Editor, *Space Medicine.* Urbana: University of Illinois Press, 1951.
McDougall, W. B., *Plant Ecology.* Philadelphia: Lea & Febiger, 1949.
Myer, B. S., and D. B. Anderson, *Plant Physiology.* New York: D. Van Nostrand, 1939.
Pescador, L., *Medicina Aeronáutica.* Madrid: Edit. Científica Médica, 1941.
Prosser, C. L., et al., *Comparative Animal Physiology.* Philadelphia: W. B. Saunders, 1950.
Puetter, A., *Handbuch d. norm. u. patholog.* In *Physiologie,* Vol. 1, p. 334. Berlin: J. Springer, 1927.
Rabinowitsch, E. I., *Photosynthesis and Related Processes.* Vol. 1. New York: Interscience Publishers, 1945.
Rippel, A., *Wachstumsgesetze.* Munich: Freising, 1925.
Ruff, S., and H. Strughold, *Grundriss der Luftfahrtmedizin.* Leipzig: J. A. Barth, 1945.
Scheer, B. T., *Comparative Physiology.* New York: Wiley & Sons, 1948.
Smith, A. L., *Lichens.* Cambridge University Press, 1921.
Tobler, F., *Die Biologie der Flechten.* Berlin: Bornträger, 1925.
White, C. S., and O. O. Benson, Jr., Editors, *Physics and Medicine of the Upper Atmosphere.* Albuquerque: University of New Mexico Press, 1952.

Articles and Papers

Benson, O. O., Jr., *The Medical Problems of Flying.* Paris: XIIIième Congrès Internationale de Médecine Militaire, etc., 1951.
Blackman, F. F., Ann. Bot., 15:185 (1928).
Bruestle, R. Z. f. Luftfahrtmedizin, 4:273 (1939).
Buettner, K. J. K., and H. Haber: *The Aeropause.* Science, 115:656 (1952).
Campbell, P. A., *Medical Aspects of Flights above the Atmosphere.* Journal of the A. M. A., 150:3 (1952).
Denzer, H., *Comparative Altitude Physiology of Animals.* German Aviation Medicine, Vol. 1, p. 321. Washington: U. S. Government Printing Office, 1950.

Doyle, W. L., *The Nutrition of the Protozoa.* Biol. Review, 18: 119 (1943).

Franck, J., *The Possibility of Photosynthesis on Mars.* In *The Atmospheres of the Earth and Planets,* Edited by G. P. Kuiper. Chicago: University of Chicago Press, 1947.

Haber, H., *The Human Body in Space.* Scientific American, 184:16-19 (1951).

Haldane, J. B. S., A. M. Kellas, and E. W. Kennaway. J. Physiol., 53:181 (1920).

Hartmann, H., G. Hepp, and U. Luft. Z. f. Luftfahrtmedizin. C:1 (1942).

Juday, K., Tr. Wisconsin Acad. Sci., Arts, and Letters, 16:1 (1908).

Luft, U. C., *Altitude Tolerance.* German Aviation Medicine, Vol. 1. Washington: U. S. Government Printing Office, 1950.

Luft, U. C., H. G. Clamann, and E. Opits, *The Latency of Hypoxia on Exposure to Altitude above 50,000 Feet.* J. of Aviation Med., 22:117 (1951).

Metz, B., J. Aviation Medicine, 22:152 (1951).

Rubin, S., M. Randall, M. Kamen, and L. L. Hyde, *Heavy Oxygen (O^{18}) as a Tracer in the Study of Photosynthesis.* J. Am. Chem. Soc., 83:877 (1941).

Seybold, A., Bot. Arch., 42:254 (1941).

Stock, H., *Triumph des Kohlenstoffes.* Naturwissenschaffen, 13: 1000 (1925).

Strughold, H., *Ecological Aspects of Planetary Atmospheres, With Special Reference to Mars.* J. of Aviation Med., 23:130 (1952).

————, *The Possibility of Life Under Extraterrestrial Conditions.* In *Symposium on Space Medicine.* Chicago: University of Illinois Press, 1950.

Strughold, H., H. Haber, K. J. K. Buettner, and F. Haber, *Where Does Space Begin?* J. of Aviation Med., 22:342 (1951).

Sweeney, H. M., *Explosive Decompression.* Air Surgeon's Bulletin, 10:1 (1944).

Turrell, F. M., Am. J. Bot., 23: 255 (1936).

INDEX

HUBERTUS STRUGHOLD,

eminent aeromedical investigator and physiologist, has spent a lifetime of research in space medicine and related studies. Since 1949 he has been head of the Department of Space Medicine, USAF School of Aviation Medicine, at Randolph Field, Texas. He was formerly Associate Professor of Physiology at the University of Wuerzburg, Associate Professor of Physiology at the University of Berlin, Director of the Aeromedical Research Institute, Berlin, and Professor of Physiology at the University of Heidelberg. He is the author of some eighty scientific papers, and co-author of a textbook on the principles of aviation medicine.

Born at Westtuennen, Westfalia, Germany, in 1898, Dr. Strughold studied at several German Universities, and served as a Research Assistant in the Department of Physiology at Western Reserve University, Cleveland, Ohio, and as a Fellow of the Rockefeller Foundation at the University of Chicago. He received his Ph.D. at the University of Muenster in 1922, and his M.D. at the University of Wuerzburg in 1924.

GREEN PEYTON

started his writing career at the age of fourteen with the publication of a story called "The Man from Atom." He has since written four books of general information, including "5,000 Miles Towards Tokyo," and "America's Heartland, The Southwest," and two novels, "Black Cabin," and "Rain on the Mountain." A native of Virginia who now lives in San Antonio, Texas, Mr. Peyton is a former editor of the magazines "Fortune," and "Time," in New York, and a former chief of the Texas bureau of "Time" and "Life." He is well known to the readers of "The New Yorker," "Holiday," "The American Mercury," and other magazines.